W9-CHI-739

RADIO
MATHEMATICS
IN
NICARAGUA

RADIO
MATHEMATICS
IN
NICARAGUA

Edited by

JAMESINE FRIEND

BARBARA SEARLE

PATRICK SUPPES

No Longer Property of
Phillips Memorial Library

INSTITUTE FOR MATHEMATICAL STUDIES

IN THE SOCIAL SCIENCES

STANFORD UNIVERSITY

Stanford, California

1980

PHILLIPS MEMORIAL
LIBRARY
PROVIDENCE, COLLEGE

QA
135.5
R216

This project was performed pursuant to a contract (AID/CM/ta−C−73−40) from the United States Agency for International Development.

The views and conclusions expressed herein are those of the authors and should not be interpreted as necessarily representing the official policies, either expressed or implied, of Stanford University or the U.S. Government.

Institute for Mathematical Studies in the Social Sciences
Ventura Hall
Stanford University
Stanford, CA 94305

Library of Congress Catalog Card Number: 80−82121
Printed in the United States of America

CONTENTS

v

FOREWORD

This is the third and final volume in a series that has described the work of the Radio Mathematics Project. The project was established in response to what has come to be known as the Congressional Mandate, the 1973 amendment to the Foreign Assistance Act that directed the United States Agency for International Development (AID) to focus its program on the "poor majority" in the least developed countries. In many countries, the rural poor live in remote areas unreached by essential social services. For the past decade, AID, in conjunction with developing countries, has been exploring the use of educational technology, and particularly radio, to increase the educational opportunities of these rural people.

This book amply documents the success of the Radio Mathematics Project in achieving its major objective of improving the quality of mathematics instruction in the primary schools of Nicaragua. As the book goes to press, the influence of the project work is being felt in such widely dispersed regions as Thailand, which is about to begin broadcasting the project's second-grade lessons, translated into Thai; the coastal region of Colombia, where a program for disadvantaged urban children is about to begin experimenting with using the tapes produced in Nicaragua; and several countries of Africa, which are going to continue the work of the project, in language arts as well as in mathematics.

Thus, our hope that the project would produce a methodology that was generalizable to other countries and to other subject matters has been realized. We hope that the timely publication of results will be useful to both projects and people who increasingly are concerned with the quality of the educational programming. We invite your comments and criticisms.

David M. Sprague

Office of Education
Development Support Bureau
Agency for International Development

xi

PREFACE

This volume reports on the work of the Radio Mathematics Project over a five-year period. The substantial accomplishments of the project during this time are due to the skillful collaboration of many people from both the United States and Nicaragua. In particular, the dedication and professional commitment of the Nicaraguan project staff were crucial ingredients of the program's success and the results of their work will reach beyond the borders of Nicaragua to benefit children in other parts of the world.

Stanford University staff members who lived and worked in Nicaragua include Project Directors Jamesine Friend and Klaus Galda as well as Thomas Tilson and Julia Ledee. Vitalia Rojas, of the Nicaraguan Ministry of Public Education, served as Co-Director. The Nicaraguan staff members were:

Irmina Cuadra de Venegas
Aldo Urbina
Amelia Talavera
David Cardoza Solis
Marvin Saballos
Mirna Osorio Rúiz
José Raúl Quintanilla
Alicia de Quintanilla
Juan José Montenegro Piñeda
José Ronaldo Pérez
Francisco Herrera Pérez
Leana Vivas de Núñez
Margarita López de Miranda
Dorys Mejía
Inez de R. Larios
Rosa Argentina Hernández
Gladys Gutiérrez López de Gámez
Elba García de Flores
Arturo Díaz
Felipe Dávila
María Auxiliadora Cerrato

Norma Guadamuz Cermeño
Sonia Centeno
Emigdio Quintero Casco
Marlene Camacho
Guillermo Bojorge
William Binns
María de los Angeles Araya
Noel Alvarez
Klemen Altamirano
Luis Ramírez Albert

Dean Jamison, now at the World Bank, contributed to the design of the original project and has continued to help shape the research effort. Several people have assisted in preparing the book. The authors are indebted to José González for text preparation, typesetting and layout, to Dianne Kanerva for editorial assistance, and to Maria Jedd for artwork.

INTRODUCTION

Jamesine Friend

IMPROVING THE QUALITY OF INSTRUCTION in the primary schools of the developing world has been the goal of many educational projects of the last decade. The United States Agency for International Development (AID), through the Development Support Bureau and the Regional Offices, has directly supported much of this work. In 1973, AID asked the Institute for Mathematical Studies in the Social Sciences (IMSSS) at Stanford University to develop a new instructional program in mathematics with radio as the medium of delivery. Moreover, IMSSS was to devise a systematic *method* for producing effective radio-based instruction that could be used by any of the developing nations to improve substantially their educational programs, in particular, mathematics instruction in rural areas and small towns, and that would be both feasible and inexpensive to distribute to such areas. To provide a context for developing this methodology and to demonstrate its efficacy, the project was to establish itself in a developing country willing to host this innovative project.

Nicaragua was chosen as the demonstration site in 1974, and the Radio Mathematics Project established an on-site office and commenced curriculum production that same year. The first Stanford staff member arrived in Nicaragua in June 1974, and the last one departed in January 1979. In the intervening four and a half years the project produced four full sets of radio-based instruction (for the first four years of primary school) and developed a well-documented, systematic methodology for the production of instructional radio programs for children.

With the departure of the Stanford staff from Nicaragua, the experimental phase of the project ended. As the continuance phase began, the Nicaraguan staff assumed the responsibility for continuing and expanding the project in Nicaragua, and the Stanford staff undertook the task of disseminating materials and information to other developing countries. The Nicaraguan project, now completely independent of the Stanford effort, is carried on under the auspices of the Nicaraguan Ministry of Public Education, with all funding provided by the government of Nicaragua; the Stanford project continues to be supported by the U.S. Agency for International Development and provides consulting and other, more active assistance to related projects in several parts of the world.

This book, the third and last of a series of volumes reporting the work of the experimental phase of the Radio Mathematics Project, includes three chapters (chaps. 1, 2, and 3) that provide a historical overview of aspects of the project. In chapter 1, José González gives a chronological description of the major events of the four and a half years of the experimental phase of the project. In chapter 2, Jamesine Friend describes the factors that influenced the design of the curriculum materials, and how and why those curriculum materials changed shape over the years. In chapter 3, Friend describes, from a historical point of view, the development of the feedback system of formative evaluation that is a vital part of the methodology developed by the project for the production of effective radio-based instruction.

The remaining chapters report the results of research conducted during the course of the project. In chapter 4, Barbara Searle and Klaus Galda present a formal evaluation of the effect of the curriculum on children's mathematical achievement, taking an overview of all four years of curriculum. In chapter 5, Edward I. George explores the effect of radio lessons on such outcomes of schooling as achievement, attendance, failure rates, within-year dropout, and re-enrollment the following school year. In chapter 6, Galda and González report the findings of an investigation into the factors Nicaraguan teachers consider when they decide which students to promote. In chapter 7, Dean Jamison expands and updates work previously reported (in Suppes, Searle, & Friend, 1978) on the determinants of student failure in Nicaragua. Finally, in chapter 8, Marvin Saballos, Galda, and González discuss a home-audience survey undertaken in the last operational year of the project.

This book, together with the previous two volumes, covers most, but not all, of the activities and research conducted in Nicaragua. One activity that will be reported separately is an investigation funded by the World Bank into the effect of textbook availability on children's achievement. In 20 classrooms at each of two grade levels, teachers were given textbooks for all the children, and the effect of this supplement on achievement was compared both to traditional instruction (with too few textbooks) and to radio-based instruction.

Another activity, or rather series of activities, that has not yet been completely documented is the investigation of the ability of Nicaraguan children in a few selected key topics in mathematics. These studies were conducted with children who received the traditional (i.e., not radio) instruction, and the aim was to provide information for curriculum design. Among the topics explored were addition, subtraction, multiplication, division, numeration, and mental arithmetic. Some of this work is reported in Friend (1979) and Sachar (1978).

Although the number of questions we have explored during the past six years is large, there are many questions that have been beyond our resources to investigate. We mention these topics here in hopes that future projects will pursue some of them. The kinds of studies we have in mind fall broadly in the category of evaluation of the impact of the project. The project has had a rather complex, multilevel goal structure. The major focus of our evaluation studies was student achievement in mathematics. We also expected the project lessons to influence attitudes of both students and teachers and perhaps other audiences as well, but for the most part our investigations of these other effects have been less systematic than our assessment of student achievement. Because most of these results have not been presented elsewhere, we review them here.

What impact did the project have on student attitudes? Did they enjoy the lessons? Were there any changes in their attitudes toward mathematics? Did the lessons help them to feel self-confident about their ability to perform mathematical tasks? Did the lessons change their attitudes toward school? toward their teacher? On the first of these questions (Did they enjoy lessons?) we have ample data from over 2,000 classroom observations to answer affirmatively: Yes, they did enjoy the lessons. But for the other questions we have little or no hard evidence. We tried quite seriously to nurture a sense of self-efficacy and to instill positive feelings toward mathematics, but apart from anecdotal evidence we cannot say how effective these efforts were.

We also have little but anecdotal evidence to answer several pertinent questions about the effect the project had on the classroom teachers. One study (Tilson & Searle, 1978) amply documented the favorable attitudes of teachers toward the use of radio for teaching mathematics, and that these attitudes became even more favorable after actual experience with radio lessons in the classroom. Tilson's (1978) in-depth, observational study of classroom occurrences showed that the radio lessons did indeed have an effect on the teachers' classroom behavior and teaching style. In particular, teachers using radio lessons divided their attention more equitably among different ability groups during the postbroadcast portion of the mathematics lessons than did teachers not using radio, and teachers using radio spent proportionally more of their time on classroom management than on instruction (since the radio was providing much of the direct instruction).

Other questions that have been asked remain unanswered, however. For example, do those teachers with faulty understanding of mathematical concepts learn mathematical content from exposure to radio programs directed at their students? (We have neither confirming nor disconfirming evidence on this issue.) Do teachers learn new pedagogical techniques from radio? (We have some anecdotal and observational evidence that they do, but the techniques they learn are sometimes imitations of techniques that are well-suited to radio but not ideal for human teachers.)

Another issue about which we know less than we would like is the extent to which, and the ways in which, teachers whom we did not observe regularly used the radio lessons. We worked closely with only a small portion of the teachers who followed the lessons. We deliberately did not visit classes included in the experimental part of the study, and as a result we are left with many unanswered questions. Did these teachers use the radio lessons? How often? Did they use the lessons in the way they were intended (as a central part of the daily mathematics lesson) or did they use them only occasionally as supplements to some more traditional curriculum? Since the lessons can have little effect on the children if they are not heard, this is a vital concern. There is much evidence that one of the major reasons for the failure of many educational radio and television projects is that the programs fall into disuse after an initial period of enthusiastic acceptance, often fostered by an energetic and influential development staff. This decline in usage may be rooted in many causes: inappropriateness of programming, difficulty in distributing printed supporting materials, unavailability of service for radio receivers, lack of funds for batteries, inadequate training of teachers. How many of these factors were also at work in Nicaragua, and how much disuse was there because of them? A systematic investigation of where, when, how often, and in what manner the radio lessons were used in schools outside our immediate sphere of influence would be both costly and time-consuming, and we would have needed a much larger staff, preferably an independent group of more disinterested observers, to answer these questions adequately.

Other groups that might have been influenced by the project are parents and other community members. Chapter 7, which describes the survey of the out-of-school audience, touches on this issue, but we did not directly investigate the attitudes of parents of children who were taking radio lessons in school. In countries like Nicaragua, this may well be one of the more important issues to investigate because the parents play a substantial role in determining which children enter school, how often they attend, and how long they remain students. Although attendance is compulsory, the law is not enforced. Many children never enroll, and many of those who do drop out after only a year or two of sometimes quite irregular attendance. The data presented in chapter 5 suggest that the school itself is not the determining factor in dropout and attendance rates, and it may well be that in Nicaragua it is parents alone who make these decisions. If so, does the availability of radio lessons have any influence? It is not inconceivable that if the parents' desire is for their children's education per se rather than for public schooling, that radio broadcasts on open frequencies could actually decrease enrollment and attendance.

Moving even further out from the classroom, did the project have an effect on school authorities, especially those in the centralized offices of the Ministry of Public Education? Was there an impact on the funding agency itself? That is, were any of its policy changes a direct or indirect result of the activities and products of the Radio Mathematics Project? Were other international agencies, such as the World Bank or UNESCO, influenced by the outcomes of the project? And finally, what effects, if any, have been and are being felt in other developing nations, especially in other projects devoted to educational radio? These are all sensitive, political issues, not amenable to analysis in the same way as children's mathematical abilities, but certainly as important to international education as any of the more specific questions we investigated within the schools of rural Nicaragua.

Despite the large number of important questions left unanswered or only partially answered, the project's evaluative investigations were sufficient to answer the questions that were most often raised when the project was being initiated. There is now no doubt that children can learn well from direct radio instruction, even subjects as conceptually complex as mathematics, and that this instruction can be delivered to remote rural areas at a cost low enough to be supportable by nations no more wealthy than Nicaragua. The children enjoy the lessons, and their teachers perceive the programs as a valued adjunct to their instructional resources. Their value is felt even outside the school where many citizens, striving to make up for their schooling deficits, listen regularly to the daily broadcasts.

Why is it that this project succeeded when others with seemingly almost identical goals failed? There are many reasons (perhaps even some we are not aware of). Primarily, we had enough money and time. It may seem strange to mention money first since our goal was to produce low-cost materials, but it is important to distinguish between development costs and implementation costs, and also between basic-research costs and product-related costs. Much of our research helped us to produce more effective lessons but should properly be written off not against the cost of producing mathematics lesson for Nicaragua but against the cost of developing the system for producing such materials, and as such was money spent toward a higher goal. As mentioned above, we would have liked to have undertaken studies of a number of interesting and important issues had the funding been available, but we were in fact amply funded for the major endeavors we were charged with.

Time, too, is an invaluable asset in such projects. It is frequently *not* the case that two people can do in one year what it would take one person two years to accomplish. With the feedback system of lesson development (described in chap. 3), a sizable crew is needed to produce one year's curriculum in one calendar year. The staff would need to be doubled to produce two years' curriculum per year, and there are no fractional possibilities with the feedback system (i.e., there is no way of using feedback to produce a half-year's curriculum in a year). This constraint of the time schedule, which we ourselves did not really understand until after the feedback system was well developed and in operation, caused us to make a drastic change in the originally negotiated time schedule. Our first contract called for the production of six years of curriculum materials, which we were to have accomplished by doubling up production after the first year in operation. As a result of our experiences with the first two grades, the contract was renegotiated to allow one year's work per year of curriculum.

Such a renegotiation was possible only because of the understanding and support the project received from its managers within the funding agency. And it was this understanding and support—in all aspects of the project, not simply the one mentioned—that was the third factor in the success of the project.

A fourth factor was the particular mix of practical and theoretical goals of the project and of the people involved. It was not simply a research project but was also aimed at producing a solid, usable product. Unlike many research projects, we did not use the Nicaraguan students purely as experimental subjects; we gave as much—in the way of improved educational opportunities—as we took—in the way of data to investigate hypotheses about the process and product of educational interventions. When we left Nicaragua, we left behind us a set of educational materials of proved value that could be used at almost no cost to improve the schooling of future hundreds of thousands of Nicaraguans. And we took with us valuable data that could contribute to all nations an improved understanding of the educational process. And finally, we devised a methodology that could be used to upgrade the educational process in other places and with other subjects.

Finally, the fifth factor contributing to the success of the project was the realism with which we approached the design of the curriculum package. We did not try to impose a new or different curriculum upon the Nicaraguan system of public education. Neither did we adopt diffuse and esoteric instructional goals. Every topic we taught was defined in concrete, behaviorally oriented terms. By applying specific goals derived from the recommendations of the Ministry of Public Education we produced noncontroversial materials with a high probability of acceptance within the established system.

We arrived at the end of our involvement with the project in Nicaragua with two regrets. The first was that we had not pushed for nationwide implementation of project lessons earlier in our work in Nicaragua. The second, related to the first, was that we had built into curriculum development the assumption that the project lessons would not be used nationwide.

As originally conceived, the project was purely developmental and experimental in nature, since at the outset we did not know that we could teach mathematics effectively by radio. After two years of field experience, it became clear that the curriculum was a great improvement over the traditional instructional method. Also, at about the same time, an independent analysis of costs (Wells & Klees, 1978) showed that "lowest costs are obtained through the most rapid implementation." Because our contract was funded specifically for research, we had no funds to commit to expansion. We therefore began working with the Ministry of Public Education to find other sources of external funding to support expansion. However, political problems and the ensuing revolution interfered with these efforts, and it is not clear that expansion will now take place. It would have been of great benefit to Nicaragua to have commenced expansion while foreign advisors were still available to help formulate plans and train the necessary staff. For future projects of a similar sort, an ideal arrangement would be to have a contingent commitment of expansion funds even before the experimental phase of the project begins.

The second aspect of the project that we now regret was the decision not to design the curriculum for a longitudinal effect. The issue, discussed more fully in chapter 2, is basically this. At the beginning of each school year we prepared lessons as if the children had never before taken radio lessons. This meant that we spent time teaching the children needed listening skills and how they were supposed to respond to various kinds of questions and tasks posed by the radio teachers. Also, we had to assume no more incoming knowledge than a child would have obtained from traditional instruction the previous year. Since the children who had taken radio lessons the preceding year were significantly ahead of those who had received traditional instruction, the net effect was to lose the value of building on past achievement. In retrospect, we should have planned for widescale use of the lessons and then worked to bring it about as soon as it was clear that it would be advantageous to do so.

The project, and especially its concrete product, the radio-based mathematics curriculum, was a success, but we see it only as a beginning. We look to future projects to surpass these efforts to improve the quality of instruction at a cost that is within the means of the developing nations of the world.

REFERENCES

Friend, J.   Column addition skills.   *Journal of Children's Mathematical Behavior,* 1979, **2,** 29–57.

Sachar, J.   Nicaraguan standardization of the Stanford Mental Arithmetic Test.   In P. Suppes, B. Searle, & J. Friend (Eds.), *The Radio Mathematics Project: Nicaragua, 1976–1977.* Stanford, Calif.: Institute for Mathematical Studies in the Social Sciences, 1978.

Suppes, P., Searle, B., & Friend, J. (Eds.).   *The Radio Mathematics Project: Nicaragua, 1976–1977.* Stanford, Calif.: Institute for Mathematical Studies in the Social Sciences, 1978.

Tilson, T.   An observation study in first-grade classrooms.   In P. Suppes, B. Searle, & J. Friend (Eds.),   *The Radio Mathematics Project: Nicaragua, 1976–1977.* Stanford, Calif.: Institute for Mathematical Studies in the Social Sciences, 1978.

Tilson, T., & Searle, B.   An assessment of teacher attitudes.   In P. Suppes, B. Searle, & J. Friend (Eds.),   *The Radio Mathematics Project: Nicaragua, 1976–1977.* Stanford, Calif.: Institute for Mathematical Studies in the Social Sciences, 1978.

Wells, S., & Klees, S.   Education decisions and cost analysis for the Radio Mathematics Project in Nicaragua.   In P. Suppes, B. Searle, & J. Friend (Eds.),   *The Radio Mathematics Project: Nicaragua, 1976–1977.* Stanford, Calif.: Institute for Mathematical Studies in the Social Sciences, 1978.

RADIO
MATHEMATICS
IN
NICARAGUA

This chapter provides a concise summary of the major events that took place in the four and a half years of the experimental phase of the Radio Mathematics Project. To fully understand the history of the project, however, it is necessary to see it in the context of the geological and political happenings of the time.

In 1972, just a year and a half before the project opened offices in Nicaragua, the city of Managua was destroyed by an earthquake. The commerical section was entirely destroyed, as were several residential areas. Almost no part of that city of 400,000 was left untouched. Over 10,000 inhabitants were killed, and many times that number evacuated to neighboring towns and villages. The social and economic effects of the earthquake were shattering. At the time the first Stanford staff members moved to Nicaragua, the city was filled with rubble, reminiscent of the views of bombed cities shown in World War II newsreels. Although the debris was largely cleared away by the time the Stanford staff left Nicaragua, no rebuilding had been done, and it is doubtful that the city will ever rise in the same location.

Politically, the country seemed quiet and stable during the first years of our residence. There were mild flurries of political activity, including a period in which all news was strictly censored, and there was a continuing low-level border dispute with the neighboring country, Costa Rica. The Costa Rican border dispute had a direct impact on the project in that our expansion to the province of Río San Juan in 1978 was largely decided by political factors. There was governmental concern that many of the people who resided along the lonely stretch of largely undeveloped territory bordering Costa Rica considered themselves almost as much Costa Rican as Nicaraguan. They felt isolated and neglected by the central Nicaraguan government. They listened to radio broadcasts from Costa Rica, had many commercial dealings with their neighbors across the border, and even occasionally sent their children to schools on the other side. In an effort to draw these people more into the larger Nicaraguan community, the government provided special services to the region, especially educational and communication services. Thus, when the Ministry of Public Education found itself with an unexpected windfall of $2,000 (the Japan Prize won by the Radio Mathematics Project), it invested that money in radio receivers for schools in Río San Juan so that children there could benefit from the mathematics programs broadcast by the Radio Mathematics Project.

By far the biggest political event of the times was the Nicaraguan revolution. This revolution was brewing even in the second year of the project, when isolated guerrilla skirmishes were reported from the hills of northern Nicaragua. It was not until January 1978 that the revolution began, with the killing of Pedro Joaquin Chamorro, editor of La Prensa, an outspoken and influential opposition newspaper. Rioting and guerrilla warfare increased in intensity, moving out of the hills and into the streets of the larger towns, including Masaya and Managua. Two general strikes closed all large stores and businesses for weeks, a strict curfew was imposed, and military forces patrolled the city. Military checkpoints were set up at all exits from Managua and on occasion in other towns, but guerrilla activity continued. In September of the same year (1978), the fighting escalated to a full-fledged revolution, which was eventually won by the revolutionaries early the following year (after the departure of American staff from the Radio Mathematics Project). The revolution left the country in an economic and social turmoil from which it has not yet recovered.

Despite the violence of the times, the Radio Mathematics Project continued to function, sometimes almost normally. We continued production and broadcasting (on all but a few days), although there were many occasions when schools in different parts of our experimental area were closed because of local fighting. Even when schools were open, the school day was often shortened, and attendance dropped dramatically. Although Masaya, where the project was located, was one of the hotspots of military activity, the fighting usually occurred in the downtown area, well removed from the project offices on the outskirts of town. Only once did the fighting become sufficiently widespread to force the staff to evacuate the office temporarily.

As the school year drew to an end, rumors that schools might be officially closed several weeks earlier than usual impelled us to embark on our posttesting program two to three weeks earlier than scheduled. Also, as travel became more dangerous we were forced to cancel a planned program of school visits.

Consequently, we did not, in the last year, collect as many data as we needed for several of the studies we had planned, and the early posttesting made comparisons with performance gains in other years somewhat questionable. However, in sum, the project was remarkably unaffected by what may be considered the bloodiest revolution (relative to the size of the country) that has taken place in Latin America in this century.

Chapter 1

A HISTORY OF
THE RADIO MATHEMATICS PROJECT

José González

BETWEEN JUNE 1973 AND DECEMBER 1978, the Institute for Mathematical Studies in the Social Sciences (IMSSS) of Stanford University,[1] the Development Support Bureau of the United States Agency for International Development (AID), and the Government of Nicaragua, represented by the Ministry of Public Education (MPE), collaborated in the development of an instructional program for use in the primary schools of Nicaragua. This chapter presents a history of that collaboration. The first section discusses the legislative and contractual origins of the Radio Mathematics Project and the selection of Nicaragua as the experimental site. Sections 2 through 7 summarize operations during the six school years (1974–1979) that the Radio Mathematics Project worked in Nicaragua. (A chronological history of the Radio Mathematics Project is presented in Appendix A.) In section 8, the characteristics, accomplishments, difficulties, and solutions of the project staff are discussed in light of the project's history.

1. ORIGINS OF THE RADIO MATHEMATICS PROJECT

The Radio Mathematics Project represents an early response by the United States Agency for International Development to a growing Congressional interest in the problems of the poor majority in developing countries. The new Congressional concern was embodied in

---

[1] IMSSS conducts research dedicated to the improvement of productivity and quality in education. Founded in 1959, it has focused its research on computer-assisted instruction in arithmetic and reading at the primary-school level; logic, set theory, and foreign languages at the undergraduate level; mathematical learning theory; and the use of technological aids in the classroom.

3

the Foreign Assistance Act of 1973, commonly called the "New Directions" legislation. Among other priorities, this legislation directed AID to increase the relevance of formal education systems to the needs of the poor, especially at the primary level, through the reform of curriculum, teaching materials, and teaching methods, and through improved teacher training (Searle & González, 1979). The Radio Mathematics Project responded directly to the second of these Congressional goals.

The Contractual Mandate

On July 1, 1973, the Technical Assistance Bureau (since renamed the Development Support Bureau) of AID contracted with IMSSS to "conduct, design, implement, and evaluate, in collaboration with developing country personnel, a prototype system of teaching elementary mathematics using radio as the major medium of instruction." The goal of the Radio Mathematics Project was the creation of a viable program of educational and technological reform capable of being managed by personnel of a developing country and of being adopted or adapted by other developing countries. As a means of achieving this goal, the Radio Mathematics Project was to develop an elementary mathematics program with radio as the instructional delivery system.

The original contract between AID and IMSSS specifically obligated IMSSS to meet the following objectives:

1. Develop and test a cost-effective prototype system of radio mathematics instruction for elementary grades in a developing country that could, with minor adaptations and translation, be used in many developing countries.

2. Develop a methodology for (a) producing radio-instructional materials based on the rapid and specific reporting of previous student responses to the materials developers and (b) using feedback on achievement and rates of learning to provide for administrative quality control.

3. Begin a program of research on major variables affecting learning through radio.

4. Help build capabilities in an appropriate institution of a developing country to continue or even expand the project with minimal further assistance from external experts.

In summary, the objectives of the Radio Mathematics Project were economic, educational, organizational, and institutional—the development of an economically feasible and educationally effective instructional system that could be generalized to other subject matters and transferred to other developing countries while concurrently meeting the educational and institutional needs of the host country.

Site-selection Process

The Radio Mathematics Project, in contrast to most AID projects, did not arise from a country's request for assistance. Rather, the initial contractual agreement between AID and IMSSS stipulated that the project find an appropriate site for its work (Searle, 1979). The early history (July 1973 to February 1974) of the Radio Mathematics Project is dominated by the recruitment of a Stanford project staff, the selection of a suitable experimental site, and the pilot testing of some taped mathematics lessons in California (see Searle, 1974a; Searle, Friend, & Suppes, 1976). The selection of a suitable experimental site was of primary importance to the success of the Radio Mathematics Project. Consequently, it was the primary activity of the first eight months of the contract.

Specifically, the project staff sought a country that was interested in the project and that saw potential usefulness for radio mathematics instruction within the context of its own educational development plans. Any potential host country would be required to enter into a full partnership with the Stanford staff in planning and operating the project. In addition, AID required that the host country contribute both financial and administrative support to the project. However, because of the project's experimental nature, the host country would not be asked for a commitment to continue the project beyond the pilot stages (Searle, 1979).

The Stanford project staff developed the following four general questions to guide them in selecting a suitable experimental site:

1. Is there interest in and acceptance of the project?
2. Was a tentative site in the country identified that meets the physical and technical requirements of the project?
3. Does the country need the Stanford team to help build its capabilities in radio instruction?
4. Is school instruction conducted in the native language of the children?

A discussion of the importance of these four questions and their applicability to the site-selection process is presented in Searle (1974b).

Three site-selection trips were made to countries in Southeast Asia, Latin America, and Africa. The visits were conducted by Professor Patrick Suppes, principal investigator of the Radio Mathematics Project and Director of IMSSS, Dr. Barbara Searle, Stanford coordinator of the project and senior research associate at IMSSS, and Dr. David Sprague, the AID contract officer in charge of the Radio Mathematics

Project. Jamesine Friend, selected as project director on February 1, 1974, replaced Suppes on the third site-selection trip.

Twelve countries in these three areas of the developing world expressed interest in learning more about the proposed project by responding to cables sent to their local AID missions. The countries visited in Southeast Asia were Indonesia, the Philippines, South Vietnam, and Thailand (September 5–19, 1973); the countries visited in Latin America were Colombia, Ecuador, Panamá, and Perú (November 8–20, 1973), and Brazil and Nicaragua (January 6–20, 1974); the countries visited in Africa were Nigeria and Swaziland (January 6–20, 1974).

In each country, the AID mission education officer arranged a series of meetings between the project staff and various political and educational officials who would be involved in establishing and operating the project. Pertinent data were collected about the educational resources of the country, ongoing educational development efforts, and the degree to which the Radio Mathematics Project could assist in the educational development of the country (and region) without unnecessarily duplicating ongoing efforts.

Selection of Nicaragua as Project Site

Of the 12 countries visited by Suppes, Searle, Sprague, and Friend, six expressed interest in participating in and collaborating with the Radio Mathematics Project; a suitable experimental site was identified in five countries; technical assistance in the area of educational development was needed in six countries; and school instruction was conducted in the native language of the children in eight countries. Two countries, Panamá and Nicaragua, were highly rated on all four criteria (Memo of Research Advisory Committee, RAC meeting, October 17–18, 1974).

As a result of the site-selection process, the project staff in cooperation with the Technical Assistance Bureau of AID selected Nicaragua as its first choice for the project site. The selection discussion was held at a joint meeting of the Stanford staff and AID in Washington, D.C., on February 8, 1974. Nicaragua was rated quite high on 11 important country-selection subfactors—the response of government officials, availability of a radio transmitter, availability of suitable schools, country-wide use of the native language (Spanish) as the language of instruction, availability of personnel trained in curriculum, availability of potential project staff, identification of an experimental site, availability of a recording studio, use of a modern mathematics curriculum, and the representative level of development and size of the country.

The tentative selection of Nicaragua as the project's first choice for the host country was communicated to its Minister of Public Education on February 15, 1974. A second staff visit to Nicaragua took place March 6–15, 1974 for further, more detailed negotiations. Participating in these negotiations were Friend, Searle, and Thomas Tilson, a Stanford staff member who would be working at the project site. The Stanford staff decided after three days of meetings that the Ministry of Public Education would be able to meet satisfactorily the requirements for personnel and radio facilities, the only areas in which there had been any doubt as to Nicaragua's suitability as a host country. Based on this follow-up visit, the Stanford project staff made a firm decision to locate the project in Nicaragua. The selection of Nicaragua as the project site was formally accepted by AID on April 1, 1974.

During the remainder of their March 1974 visit, the Stanford staff recruited several Nicaraguan staff members, visited local schools, completed arrangements for an experimental site, and obtained initial demographic data on Nicaraguan students and schools. In addition, preliminary steps were taken to secure a project office in the experimental area and to find housing for the Stanford staff and their families.

As a result of these negotiations, the project was located in the province of Masaya, approximately 30 kilometers southeast of Managua. The province has an area of 543 square kilometers and is the smallest of the 16 provinces in the country. In 1974 the province had a population of 94,000; approximately one-third of the population lived in the city of Masaya, the capital of the province.

Among the organizational matters settled during these negotiations was the status of the Radio Mathematics Project within the existing educational bureaucracy in Nicaragua. It was agreed that the project would fall administratively under the jurisdiction of the Research and Evaluation Department (Departamento de Investigación y Evaluación Educativa), a newly established research unit within the Office of Planning (Oficina de Planeamiento Integral) of the Ministry of Public Education. The Office of Planning was responsible for all curriculum development, evaluation of curricular goals, and experimental projects (Searle, 1979). The Research and Evaluation Department had been organized just before the project's involvement in Nicaragua and agreed to work closely with the project. The Director of the Office of Planning was granted administrative responsibility (Searle, 1974a). However, it was the responsibility of the Minister of Education to request the cooperation of each Provincial School Inspector involved in the project. In other words, work would be coordinated centrally, rather than by cooperation between provinces.

The original Nicaraguan staff members assigned to the Radio Mathematics Project were already employed by the Ministry and needed only to be transferred. During the period prior to the establishment of a functioning project office in Nicaragua, the Ministry accepted responsibility for and successfully recruited additional staff members. Indeed, there was much active Ministry involvement during the interim period between site selection and the arrival of the Stanford staff. Much of the initial responsibility for the work was given to Nicaraguan staff members from the inception of the project.

Formal Agreement Between AID and MPE

A formal agreement between AID and the Ministry was signed April 1, 1974. The agreement (AGREEMENT No. 1–74 MEP and AID) was unusual in that, as it explicitly states,

> the project is designed to produce results that will not only be directly beneficial to the educational system of Nicaragua but will serve as a model for other countries as well. . . . The first application of this system is the development of a primary-level mathematics course in Nicaragua. The system for developing instructional materials is expected to be applicable to other subject matters and to other countries. The mathematics curriculum materials developed during the course of the project will be usable, with minor modifications, in other countries.

In agreeing to host the Radio Mathematics Project, the Ministry assumed a subsidiary role. It agreed to assist AID and IMSSS to establish a project that would benefit not only Nicaragua, but also the remainder of Latin America and other developing countries throughout the world. The agreement between the Ministry and AID states further that

> the Ministry of Public Education . . . in cooperating in this project will add staff and other support to the implementing agent (i.e., IMSSS) for carrying out the objectives of this project.

Usually, a developing country initiates a project and requests assistance in meeting the goals and objectives of that project from outside organizations. In contrast, the Ministry agreed that "although (the project) will be a joint effort, Stanford will bear final responsibility for its successful completion." IMSSS at Stanford, not the Ministry, was the implementing agent.

In meeting its obligations, the Ministry agreed to provide *counterpart* staff and support materials for carrying out the objectives of the experimental project. However, the mechanism for transferring staff members into and out of the project was not discussed. Legally, the Ministry retained final authority over Nicaraguan staff members, since it was paying their salaries. Administratively, however, Project Director Friend was empowered to make recommendations concerning staff changes.

The Ministry retained control over major decisions such as course content (the mathematical content of the project lessons is based on the official Nicaragua Ministry of Education curriculum), location of the experimental program, and the rate and direction of expanded coverage. Specifically, the Ministry and AID agreed that only if the project proved to be successful in meeting the educational needs of Nicaraguan primary-school children would the Nicaraguan government consider its adoption beyond the pilot phase and extension beyond the limited geographical area of the experiment (Searle & González, 1979). The Ministry also agreed to provide salaries for a substantial portion of the staff, office furniture and rent, transmitting facilities, and, increasingly in later years, funds for office supplies. Most operating expenses were covered by Stanford through a funding mechanism that did not involve the Ministry (Searle, 1979).

The degree of responsibility and autonomy granted the Radio Mathematics Project staff was unusual for development projects and unique in Nicaraguan history. In general, the project was free of day-to-day direction by the Ministry. The experimental nature of the program and the absence of prior Nicaraguan experience with instructional radio were considered justification for the lack of administrative parity between Nicaraguan and Stanford personnel (Searle, 1979).

In summary, prior to the selection of a country in which to work, the Radio Mathematics Project staff members were concerned with the issue of transferability (contractually required) and with finding an organizational niche in the bureaucracy of the host country. The ease of the latter would contribute to the internal success of the project in the country that would eventually be selected as the project site. Also, the selection of an organizational framework that was not unique to the host country, but, rather, typical of the region and of developing countries in general, would enhance the project's eventual transferability. In other words, while the project staff desired a cooperative organizational relationship between the Radio Mathematics Project and the host country, one in which the project and the host government would mutually benefit, they were hesitant to have the unique characteristics of the project sacrificed to fit into the host bureaucracy. On the other hand, as was emphasized above, the project staff was eager to establish the project in an environment where its chances of succeeding were good. The accomplishment of both these objectives contributed substantially to the eventual success of the Radio Mathematics Project.

2. THE 1974 SCHOOL YEAR

Arrival of Stanford Staff Members in Nicaragua

The original Stanford staff members of the Radio Mathematics Project in Nicaragua were Project Director Jamesine Friend, Thomas Tilson, and Julia Ledee, an expert in radio broadcasting. The Stanford staff members arrived in Nicaragua in June 1974, the middle of the 1974 school year in Nicaragua.[2] For several weeks prior to their arrival (April 1 to May 10, 1974), Friend and Tilson attended language classes and AID orientation meetings in Washington, D.C. Ledee was already fluent in Spanish.

Most of the summer of 1974 was devoted to organizational tasks, primarily establishing a project office in Masaya; recruiting, hiring, and training Nicaraguan staff members; and making final arrangements for the use of recording and computing facilities. Several more substantial activities were also begun—developing and administering tests of mathematics achievement to first-grade students at the end of the 1974 school year, gathering data on students and schools, selecting experimental (radio) and control (traditional) classes, writing and pilot-testing a set of six radio lessons, and arranging for daily radio lessons in 16 experimental (radio) schools in the following school year. Some of this work had been completed by the Nicaraguan staff members assigned to the Radio Mathematics Project by the Ministry before the arrival of the Stanford staff. For example, Nicaraguan staff members designed and wrote a preliminary version of a mathematics achievement test for first-grade students. The test was subsequently revised based on results from field tests conducted after the Stanford staff arrived in Nicaragua. However, it should be noted that even prior to the arrival of the expatriate staff, Nicaraguan staff members were active in the operation of the project (Searle, 1974a).

Establishment of a Project Office

One of the first tasks of the project staff was to situate the project offices in a suitable building. The offices (in the Institute of Masaya, a secondary school in downtown Masaya) arranged for during the negotiation visit in March 1974 seemed unsatisfactory at second sight. A more acceptable location, a three-bedroom house on the outskirts of Masaya, was found within a month after the arrival of the Stanford

---

[2] The Nicaraguan school year runs from February through November.

staff members. Unlike the Institute, this building needed no major alterations or renovation. As outlined above, the Ministry paid the rent and some of the utilities; all other office costs were paid by the project.

The Masaya office of the Radio Mathematics Project was officially opened on July 4, 1974. The project office was furnished haphazardly during the second half of the 1974 school year, as no funds had been allocated in the 1974 Ministry budget for additional office furniture and supplies. Instead, the project office used discarded school desks and office furniture. In January 1975, the Ministry provided the project with a large complement of new furniture.

From June 1974 to March 1975, the necessary office machinery was either shipped to the project from the United States (e.g., mimeograph machine) or rented locally (e.g., Xerox machine, IBM keypunch). Office supplies were purchased locally; almost all the supplies and supplemental equipment used for radio production were imported from the United States, but the basic recording equipment was already available in a local radio station. Finally, four vehicles were imported from the United States. These vehicles were used heavily for visiting classes, educational testing, running errands, and transporting staff members daily from Managua to Masaya. Three of the vehicles were four-wheel drive, necessary to visit relatively inaccessible schools.

Establishing a Project Staff

Recruiting and training staff members occupied much of the time of the Stanford staff during the first months of the project's operation in Nicaragua. As has been described above, the initial Stanford staff consisted of Project Director Friend (who doubled as curriculum specialist), Fieldwork Director Tilson, and Radio Producer-Director Ledee. The first two Nicaraguan staff members—Vitalia Rojas de Vrooman, the Nicaraguan codirector, and David Cardoza, a curriculum writer—were assigned to the project by the Ministry in March 1974 and devoted over half of their time between March and June to the project. Both had been curriculum specialists at the Ministry. Vrooman had been involved in the recent revision of the Nicaraguan mathematics curriculum and had worked previously in a book-development project sponsored by ROCAP, the Regional Organization for Central America and Panamá. Luis Ramírez, a professor of educational research, was later added to the project staff (Searle, 1979). These individuals were the only Nicaraguan professionals initially available to the project who had training in areas related to project work.

Beyond the Ministry experts who joined the project at the outset, all curriculum personnel and scriptwriters were trained by the project. These training activities proved to be time-consuming, but within a year, the project had a fully functioning Nicaraguan staff.

The personnel problems were less severe in classroom observation and teacher training. After early problems, production of instructional materials (e.g., worksheets, teacher's guides) ran smoothly under the direction of Juan José Montenegro. Montenegro was also the Nicaraguan counterpart director for teacher training, working with Tilson, the fieldwork director. Finally, research functions, including classroom testing, were jointly administered by Tilson and Ramírez.

By the end of the first year of operation there were 23 Nicaraguans on the staff—11 professionals and the remainder support staff. The staff consisted of six teams, each headed by one of the expatriates: Friend was leader of the administrative, curriculum development, and support teams; Tilson was leader of the research and teacher-training teams; and Ledee was leader of the production team. Nicaraguans served as team members, with one of the nationals serving as a counterpart to the expatriate team leader.

Pilot-testing of Radio Lessons

The months of September through November 1974 (the end of the 1974 school year) were used to write, record, and pilot-test a set of six radio lessons for the 1975 school year. Preliminary information about many aspects of the design of radio lessons was obtained from the administration of these pilot radio lessons to first-grade classrooms at the end of the 1974 school year.

Preparation of the pilot lessons also gave the staff an opportunity to work out many of the procedures that would be necessary for producing lessons on a tight schedule. Initially, two lessons were written, tested in three classrooms, and then completely rewritten. Four more lessons were subsequently produced. All six lessons comprised the set of pilot lessons given in six classrooms during November 1974. The characteristics and design of these lessons are described in detail in Searle, Friend, and Suppes (1975).

Other Research Activities

In addition to the establishment of a project office and staff, and the design and pilot-testing of six radio lessons, the Radio Mathematics Project conducted several other supplementary research activities during its first year in Nicaragua—administering a mathematics achievement test, administering an attitude questionnaire to first-grade teachers, and studying the determinants of repetition and dropout in Nicaragua. (For the details about these research activities, see the references at the end of this chapter.) The mathematics achievement test was administered in October and November, 1974, to 44 first-grade classes. Overlapping this activity during late October and early November, teacher questionnaires were distributed to and interviews conducted with 44 first-grade teachers. Supplementary research activities like these would continue throughout the history of the Radio Mathematics Project in Nicaragua.

3. THE 1975 SCHOOL YEAR

First-grade Instructional Program

Early plans had called for the first-grade instructional program to begin during the middle of the 1974 school year but the project was unable to begin producing lessons as soon as the staff had hoped. The time needed to locate and establish an office and to recruit and train staff members had been underestimated. Thus, although Stanford staff members arrived in Nicaragua in June 1974, it was August (the seventh month of the school year) before the project was able to begin serious work on the writing of lessons.

Curriculum development. Curriculum development and planning for the opening of school occupied the months before mid-February 1975 (the opening of the 1975 school year in Nicaragua). Sixteen first-grade classrooms were selected to participate in the initial experimental program. Radio lessons[3] were not initiated at the very start of the 1975 school year, however. Instead, the project staff decided to provide three weeks of "readiness" material to prepare children to use worksheets and to familiarize them with the vocabulary and response modes the radio would ask of them.

During the first four weeks of school, only three radio lessons per week (instead of the five daily lessons planned) were presented to the children. The inexperience of the project production staff precluded the possibility of producing the five lessons per week. Lessons were not prepared in advance also because of the need to respond rapidly to experience with the earliest lessons. However, after the first four weeks, a radio lesson was produced for and presented on each school

---

[3] Because of the experimental nature of the first-grade instructional program developed during the 1975 school year, all radio lessons were recorded on cassette tapes and presented in classrooms using battery-operated tape recorders rather than broadcast via the radio.

day. By the end of the 1975 school year in November, 150 first-grade lessons had been produced and presented to the children.

Teacher training. Project teachers met weekly for the first month of school and thereafter approximately once every six weeks. The initial set of teacher-training sessions was designed to acquaint teachers with the purposes of the project, help them become oriented to their new teaching role, allow the project staff and teachers to become acquainted, explain logistical aspects of the project (i.e., distribution and collection of materials, classroom observation schedules), present specific teaching plans for the project lessons they were being asked to use, and gather teacher reactions to using radio in the classroom.

Classroom observation. Project staff members observed the mathematics lessons daily in six classrooms and weekly in five of the 16 classrooms. The remaining five classrooms were not observed at all in order to find out the kinds of problems that would arise, how well the teacher would be able to cope with them, and whether such classes used the recorded lessons as regularly as those that were observed. Project-developed observation forms were used by project-trained classroom observers. All members of the professional staff, including the curriculum developers, the scriptwriters, and the radio producer-director, were required to visit classrooms on a regular basis to gain a more complete understanding of the effect of the radio lessons in the classrooms (Friend, 1976a, 1976b, 1976c). Classroom observations, together with the examination of performance data from student worksheets and tests, stimulated changes in the radio lessons.

Summative evaluation. The first-grade pretest was a modified version of the *Test of Basic Experiences* (TOBE). It was given to 537 children in the 16 experimental schools in early March, 1975, and to 268 students in the 9 control schools that were randomly selected from among those not participating in the project in early April, 1975. At the end of the 1975 school year (during late October and early November), the project staff administered posttests to randomly selected first- and second-grade classrooms, distributed teacher questionnaires, and conducted teacher interviews.

Project expansion. In May 1975, at the suggestion of the Ministry, six classrooms in the neighboring province of Granada were included in the already expanding experimental program. Radio lessons in Granada schools were used without direct supervision by the project staff. Materials were delivered to the School Inspector, who, in turn, delivered them to the teachers involved in the program. The School Inspector also provided teacher training after consultation with the teacher-training staff in Masaya.

The Origins of Formative Evaluation

First-grade lessons presented to the children in the 1975 school year were accompanied by student worksheets. The worksheets were collected at the end of each lesson and analyzed. The worksheet data, together with the classroom observations described above, were used to evaluate the effectiveness of the radio lessons and to modify parts of the lesson design that seemed ineffective. If the worksheets indicated that the students were not learning certain mathematical topics at the rate the project staff had hoped, future lessons could provide additional instruction and practice. In addition, by examining the errors made by students on the worksheets, the project staff could analyze where the previous radio lessons needed improvement. Thus, use of student worksheets and analysis of student errors were the first methods of feedback used by the Radio Mathematics Project.

The examination of student worksheets as one source of information for revising lessons was abandoned during the 1975 school year. It was replaced by a system of tests embedded in the lessons and finally, in August 1975, by a system of weekly paper-and-pencil tests. (The use of embedded tests is described in chap. 3; the use of weekly paper-and-pencil tests is described in Galda & de Quintanilla, 1978.) Worksheet data proved to be insufficient for several reasons. First, the radio gave many of the correct answers as reinforcement. The project staff consequently could not be certain that the responses on the worksheets accurately reflected what the children had learned, since the children might have written the correct answer after it was given to them by the radio. Second, the lesson items did not directly test many concepts that had been taught in previous lessons. Thus, the project staff could not measure the retention of previously learned material. Third, the children were given so much instruction before the item or as they were doing the item that the project staff could not determine how well the children could have done the work on their own. Fourth, there were no items on concepts that had not already been introduced. Thus, the project staff could not find out how much the children knew before instruction on those concepts was begun. (A more complete discussion of these reasons is included in chap. 3.) Finally, worksheets proved to be too expensive. Consistent with its mandate to produce lessons that would be inexpensive to use, the project staff recommended that the entire first-grade instructional program be revised to eliminate the use of worksheets. (The latter third of the first-grade instructional program was eventually revised to be presented without worksheets. Results of this worksheet experiment and the revision of the first-grade instructional program are described in Galda, González, Searle, & Friend, 1979.)

4. THE 1976 SCHOOL YEAR

Two major lesson-development tasks were undertaken during 1976—development of lessons for the second grade and revision of lessons for the first grade. For the first time, lessons were broadcast over the radio. Project lessons for the 1976 school year were initiated on February 16, 1976, shortly after the opening of school. Second-grade lessons were broadcast at 8:30 A.M. and first-grade lessons at 9:45 A.M. on the national radio station, Radiodifusora Nacional de Nicaragua. This was a government-owned radio station; air time was provided free of charge to the project. The 1976 school year ended on November 18, 1976 with the presentation of Lesson 25 of the second-grade program to the first-grade classrooms (the last lesson of the first-grade program, Lesson 150, was broadcast to the first-grade classrooms on October 13, 1976) and Lesson 175 to the second-grade classrooms.

The use of radio lessons was expanded to three provinces during the 1976 school year—the provinces of Masaya, Granada, and Carazo. The experimental area was expanded to increase the number of schools from which to draw classes and to accommodate some of the teachers in neighboring areas who had expressed interest in using the project mathematics lessons.

The 1976 First-grade Instructional Program

A revised version of the 1975 first-grade program was used during the 1976 school year. Eight new radio lessons were produced to complete the sequence of the early lessons (the first four weeks of the 1975 program, in which only three lessons instead of five were used per week). The remaining lessons were completely revised. The project worked with 45 first-grade classrooms during the 1976 school year, of which 30 were selected at random from rural and urban schools in Masaya, Granada, and Carazo.

Lesson materials were produced at the project office in Masaya. Approximately 40,000 copies of the worksheets and 900 copies of the teacher's guides for the first-grade program were produced and distributed monthly. The 1975 teacher's guide was completely rewritten. Student worksheets were changed only where pictures were found to be confusing or where errors had been made in the previous version. Both the teacher's guides and the student worksheets for the first-grade program were distributed through the Inspector's Office in the local province. Teachers were asked to collect these materials at the time they collected their monthly paychecks.

During the 1976 school year the project staff members attempted to maintain a greater distance between themselves and the project teachers in order to simulate closely the necessarily increased independence of teachers in a wide-scale use of the program. Thus, only two teacher-training sessions were held at the beginning of the school year during February and March, 1976. Also, of the 45 first-grade classes participating in the radio program in 1976, only five classes were observed regularly and six classrooms were tested weekly.

The first-grade classrooms were pretested in the period between February 23 and March 29, 1976, at the beginning of the school year. At the end of the 1976 school year, during late October and early November, 1976, the project staff administered posttests to 53 first-grade classrooms. A complete description of the first-grade testing program and results of this first formal evaluation of the Radio Mathematics Program is provided in Searle, Matthews, Suppes, and Friend (1978) and in chapter 4 of this volume.

The 1976 Second-grade Instructional Program

The second-grade instructional program was developed during the 1976 school year. Twenty second-grade classes in the province of Masaya participated in the experimental program in 1976. In addition, 20 teachers in neighboring provinces who asked to use the second-grade lessons were included. (These teachers, as well as all subsequent voluntary teachers, were not part of the formal evaluation of the experiment, as they were not randomly selected.) In all, some 1,400 second-grade children listened to the instructional radio programs in 1976.

The second-grade lessons did not use student worksheets; rather, teachers were asked to copy exercises from the teacher's guide onto the chalkboard before the radio broadcast. The children used their notebooks for written work. Copies of the teacher's guide for the second-grade program were distributed weekly. As with first-grade teachers, second-grade teachers were asked to pick up the materials themselves. Radios and copies of the teacher's guide were supplied to all 40 teachers by the project. In 38 schools the radios were shared with first-grade classrooms. Except for the use of the national radio station rather than cassette tape recorders for playing the lessons, the second-grade lessons were presented in much the same way as the 1975 first-grade lessons.

For the same reasons as discussed above for the first-grade program, only five second-grade classrooms were observed at least twice a week, the remaining classes only occasionally. Two teacher-training sessions were held at the the start of the school year, none subsequently. Pretests were administered to 44 (24 control and 20 experimental) second-grade classes in March and April, 1976. Third-grade control classes were also pretested in March and April; some fourth-grade classes were pretested in April 1976. At the end of the 1976 school year, during late October and early November, 1976, the project staff administered posttests to 46 second-grade, 24 third-grade, and 12 fourth-grade classes. Results of these tests are presented in chapter 4 of this volume.

Radio Broadcast Difficulties

The project staff maintained a schedule of preparing, producing, and broadcasting a lesson each day of the school year for each grade level. However, transmission difficulties plagued the first year of actually broadcasting the lessons—primarily errors in transmission (e.g., playing a lesson on the wrong day) or disruptions (e.g., preemptions by other programs, power failures, and equipment failures).

The project staff took several steps to rectify these errors. A staff member was assigned to be at the recording studio each morning to deliver personally the correct tape to the radio station and to see that the announcements were read at the proper time. First-grade lessons, which were broadcast later in the morning, were disrupted particularly often. Various government officials were notified, and by the end of the school year these problems had decreased in severity. In addition, the time of the first-grade lessons was changed in June from 9:45 A.M. to 9:00 A.M. to avoid preemptions by political broadcasts that were more likely to occur somewhat later in the morning.

Initiation of Fast-feedback Scheme

The 1976 school year witnessed the further development of the systematic use of observation and performance data (jointly called feedback) in lesson development. Two components of the lessons were affected by feedback: curriculum content and lesson format. Observations were the most useful source of information about aspects of lesson format; the program of weekly pencil-and-paper tests started late in 1975 was used to collect performance data. The advantage of this scheme for using test data to direct curriculum development was that misjudgments could be corrected during the development of the instructional program. Producing lessons with fast feedback, as this scheme came to be called, required a tight production schedule and consequently tighter administrative control of the project. (For a more complete description of the fast-feedback system and its application and development by the Radio Mathematics Project, see Friend, 1976a, 1976b, 1976c, and chap. 3.)

Other Research Activities

Besides implementing the first- and second-grade instructional programs and testing first- through fourth-grade classrooms, the project staff also carried out preliminary curriculum work for the third-grade program during the 1976 school year. In addition, as in the previous school years, the project staff distributed questionnaires to teachers to assess their attitudes toward the project and collected student dropout and repetition data. Reports of these activities are available in Tilson and Searle (1978) and Jamison (1978). Finally, a test of addition and subtraction skills was administered to 2,000 first-through fourth-grade students in August and to 1,000 fifth- and sixth-grade students in September. The tests and results are discussed in Searle, Friend, Suppes, and Tilson (1977), Tilson, Searle, Friend, and Suppes (1978), and Friend (1979).

Dissemination Activities

The first dissemination activities of the Radio Mathematics Project took place during the second half of the 1976 school year. On August 4, 1976, the Nicaraguan staff members of the project made a presentation to school inspectors and subinspectors at the Ministry of Public Education in Managua. Approximately a month later, in early September, 1976, the Radio Mathematics Project sponsored an International Conference on the Use of Radio as an Instructional Tool in Primary Schools. The conference took place at the Central American Graduate School of Business in Managua, Nicaragua. The conference was attended by 14 participants from 11 different developing countries, by project staff members, and by guests from the United States. (Meetings were conducted in both Spanish and English, using simultaneous translation.) The major goal of the conference was to share project methods and results with educators from developing countries. Five Nicaraguan staff members and three Stanford staff members presented papers at the conference ranging from a general description of the project activities to a detailed examination of the formative evaluation system developed by the project. The conference provided simultaneous translation to allow participation of all Nicaraguan staff members regardless of their knowledge of English. Finally, a seminar on the Radio Mathematics Project was held in Masaya in early December, 1976, for Ministry of Public Education and Nicaraguan university personnel.

In addition to the dissemination activities described above, IMSSS published its first summary volume—Searle, Friend, and Suppes

(1976)—concerning the activities of the first two years of the Radio Mathematics Project's work in Nicaragua on November 1, 1976. This volume was distributed widely in the United States and to many countries throughout the world.

5. THE 1977 SCHOOL YEAR

The 1977 Second- and Third-grade Instructional Programs

The major new task of 1977 was the development of lessons for the third grade. The Radio Mathematics Project began broadcasting lessons to 55 second-grade and 60 third-grade classes on February 28, the first day of the 1977 school year. The second-grade lessons were essentially the same as those broadcast the previous year. The third-grade lessons were developed during the 1977 school year using the by now well-developed formative evaluation (fast feedback) system. First-grade lessons were not broadcast during the 1977 school year pending a decision on the use of worksheets and a revision of the first-grade instructional program. The 1977 school year ended on November 18 with the broadcast of Lesson 164 to second- and third-grade classes.

Teacher training. One teacher-training session was conducted for second- and third-grade teachers in each of the provinces participating in the project in 1977—Masaya, Granada, and Carazo. The teacher-training sessions were held before the school year began in early February 1977. The second-grade teacher's guide was revised and published in two parts for distribution to the teachers. The project staff also wrote, reproduced, and distributed a third-grade teacher's guide.

Formative evaluation. Formative evaluation activities consisting of classroom observations and weekly testing were conducted only for the third-grade lessons in 1977. Twelve third-grade classes participated in the observation and weekly testing programs. Second-grade classes were neither observed nor tested, as these lessons were not going to be revised.

The formative evaluation system itself was further revised and developed during the 1977 school year. Summarizing the observation data in a form that was useful to the curriculum development team had been a continual source of difficulty. At the beginning of the 1977 school year, a daily summary was prepared from individual observation sheets. This system was time-consuming and was replaced in July 1977. Under the new scheme each observer was asked to record his or her observations directly on a master summary sheet. With this procedure, the observation data were available in concise form on the same day the lesson was broadcast. Thus, information regarding lessons could be fed to the curriculum group much more rapidly. Near the end of the year, a weekly summary system was established to condense the voluminous unedited reports and to draw special attention in a brief form to the important comments. This system proved satisfactory and was continued through the remainder of the year.

Summative evaluation. Pretests were given at the beginning of the 1977 school year to 18 second-grade, 36 third-grade, and 24 fourth-grade classes. The fourth-grade classes were evenly distributed among the three provinces working with the project, with three urban and five rural classes chosen in each province. A ratio of three urban to five rural classes was used in selecting participating classrooms in the upper grades because of the declining enrollments in the rural upper grades. An additional 43 classes in the second and fourth grades served as control classes for the formal (summative) evaluation of the programs and were pretested but did not use the radio lessons.

Third-grade lessons were formally evaluated during the 1977 school year, the same year the lessons were developed. Because the fast-feedback system allowed the development of an effective mathematics curriculum in one academic year, both formative and summative evaluations could be effectively and successfully conducted during the same year. Results of the third-grade and the second-grade summative evaluations conducted during the 1977 school year are reported in chapter 4 of this volume.

Longitudinal Study of Project Outcomes

A major activity of the Radio Mathematics Project beginning during the 1977 school year was a study of the longitudinal effects of instructional radio on student achievement in mathematics. Both second- and third-grade students participated in this study. Two groups of experimental students, designated experienced and nonexperienced, were chosen to receive second-grade lessons during the 1977 school year. The 24 classes in the experienced group were selected at random from the 30 randomly selected classes that used the first-grade lessons during the 1976 school year. The nonexperienced group contained 18 classes chosen from among those classes that had not worked with the project in the past.

As with the second grade, the third-grade classes were selected with and without previous radio experience. The experienced group of classes met all the following requirements:

1. The school had been randomly designated as experimental;
2. The class used the second-grade radio lessons in 1976;
3. The children were pretested and posttested in 1976.

Only nine schools, all in Masaya, met these requirements. One of these schools closed during the year, leaving five urban and three rural schools. The nonexperienced classes were taken at random from the list of eligible experimental schools. Details of the longitudinal effects of radio mathematics instruction are presented in chapter 4.

Río San Juan Implementation

During the early part of the 1977 school year, the Minister of Public Education expressed her interest in expanding the use of project lessons into the province of Río San Juan, a thinly populated, largely undeveloped rural area stretching along the Costa Rican border between Lake Nicaragua and the Caribbean. The project staff gave its full cooperation to the Ministry in formulating plans for expanding the program. However, some concern was expressed about the feasibility of starting lessons part of the way into the school year. The concern was that the children might have difficulty in following instructions, having missed some of the readiness material incorporated into the early lessons, and that they would not have covered enough of the prerequisite material to be able to follow the lessons.

In order to test the feasibility of starting radio lessons in the middle of the year, the staff conducted a brief trial in a rural school near the project office. Taped radio lessons were presented to both second and third grades for three consecutive days during May 1977. The children were given a very brief introduction: They were told that the tape recorder would give them instructions about mathematics and that they would have to respond both orally and in their notebooks. Two staff members monitored the lessons and gave individual help to students who appeared to need it.

Contrary to staff expectations, the children did very well. After three days they were responding, both orally and in writing, fully as well as the average radio class that had started at the beginning of the year. However, it was clear from observation that this school was not representative of the rural schools in Río San Juan. Although this experiment was successful, the Minister and project staff members agreed to delay the implementation of the project lessons in Río San Juan until the beginning of the 1978 school year.

The Japan Prize

In April 1976, the project initiated inquiries about submitting an entry for the 11th Japan Prize International Educational Program Contest which was to be held in Tokyo in February 1977. A typical lesson (Lesson 171) of the second-grade program was selected and submitted to the contest on behalf of the Nicaraguan Ministry of Education. On March 1, 1977, the Ministry was notified that the project lesson had won the Japan Prize for radio. The Minister of Public Education decided that the prize money (US$2,000) would be used to purchase radios and materials for the future implementation of the project lessons in Río San Juan.

Other Research Activities

As part of the formal summative evaluation activities during the second half of the 1977 school year, the project staff made unannounced visits to selected second- and third-grade classes in September and October. The purpose of these visits was to determine how many of the radio classes were listening to the broadcasts on a regular basis. The project staff members making these visits found that a majority of the classes were listening to the radio lessons regularly. Details of this activity are discussed in Searle et al. (1978).

The collection and analysis of school and demographic data were continued during the year for the project's continuing research into the patterns of educational wastage in Nicaragua. Data collected in 1976 and 1977 are reported in chapter 5. Also, under the auspices of EDUTEL, a private consulting firm (funded by an AID contract), a cost analysis of the Radio Mathematics Project was conducted by Dr. Stuart Wells of San José State University. The results of this study are reported in Wells and Klees (1978).

Project Administration

By the end of the original contract period, June 30, 1977, the office could be considered fully staffed; the project staff included two expatriate North Americans and 28 full-time Nicaraguans. (The third expatriate, Ledee, left the project when her Nicaraguan counterpart had successfully learned the production process.) In addition, seven people worked part time as actors and production technicians. By this time, almost all substantive activities were done by Nicaraguans, and the Stanford staff members moved increasingly into positions of technical advisors on matters of curriculum development and research design. In addition, administrative procedures and organizational concerns were fairly stable by the end of the original contract period.

The project office was organized into six major departments—curriculum, radio production, research and evaluation, teacher training, materials production, and support—supervised by department managers. However, almost everyone on the staff performed more than one function that often fell into more than one department. Furthermore, many staff members changed jobs to learn about many different aspects of the production process. In particular, scriptwriters and curriculum-development personnel were encouraged to observe classes to gain a better understanding of the way in which the project materials were used in the classroom by the children (see Friend, 1976a, 1976b, 1976c).

The lesson-production process had the following steps: curriculum design, preparation of lesson outlines, instruction writing, entertainment writing, preparation of the finished script, writing of the teacher's guide, art work, final checking of the script, and direction and production of the recorded lesson. These tasks were handled by the curriculum and scriptwriting departments. The teacher-training assistant wrote the teacher's guide.

At the next stage, the lessons were broadcast in the classrooms and data collection began. Classrooms were observed, observation summaries prepared, children tested, data analyzed, and recommendations made for changes in future lesson design. These activities were the responsibility of the research and evaluation department.

The support staff included three secretaries, an artist, a gardener, a night guard, and two maids. In addition, a bookkeeper handled business matters for the project. (Initially, Project Director Friend personally handled the financial matters of the project, but her other duties became too numerous to allow her to continue doing so.)

At the end of the original contract period in June 1977, this team of 30 people produced one new lesson each school day for the instructional program under development (e.g., the third-grade instructional program during the 1977 school year). In addition, a lower level of activity supported the presentation and evaluation of lessons from a previously developed instructional program (e.g., the second-grade instructional program during the 1977 school year). However, the primary activity of the majority of the project staff was the development of that school year's instructional program.

Project Extension

On June 22, 1977, the Ministry and AID signed a new contract and agreement to extend the Radio Mathematics Project for two years, from July 1, 1977 to June 30, 1979. Under the new agreement, Stanford's participation in Nicaragua was scheduled to end on December 31, 1978. (The details of this agreement are summarized in sec. 1.) Through the new agreement between AID and the Ministry, the government of Nicaragua demonstrated its support of the project's work by substantially increasing its commitment to the project.

The acceptance of new obligations by the Nicaraguan government underscored their strong support of the effort and indicated their intention to eventually extend the project nationwide.

A major objective of the project extension agreement was to prepare for the wide-scale implementation of the radio lessons in Nicaragua. In 1977 the project collected and organized the necessary data to determine the reception costs for implementing the project for each grade in each of the 16 provinces of Nicaragua. Finding the funding for such a major expansion of the project was the major obstacle to the wide-scale implementation of the Radio Mathematics Project. The Ministry tried to find the necessary funding internally. Unfortunately, political disturbances increased during the year, negating any efforts to expand the Radio Mathematics Project on a national scale.

Despite these difficulties, the project staff continued to prepare the program for its eventual use in all parts of Nicaragua. For example, a major trend throughout the first three years of the Radio Mathematics Project was the gradual reduction of the support materials necessary for the successful use of the radio lessons. There was a dual motivation for this reduction. Economically, requiring fewer support materials for the successful implementation of the radio lessons would make them less expensive, thereby facilitating their wide-scale use in a developing country such as Nicaragua. In a practical sense, having to use fewer support materials would ease the logistical problems of distributing the materials that would arise in a wide-scale (e.g., national) implementation of the radio lessons. In addition, fewer support materials would make the radio lessons more accessible to a nonformal, out-of-school audience. The possibility of using the radio lessons in a nonformal school setting had arisen in discussions at the international conference mentioned earlier. These three concerns motivated the project staff to eliminate gradually the necessity of any support materials from the design of the radio lessons. Historically, this trend is exhibited by the first-grade program's reliance on worksheets, the second-grade program's reliance on the chalkboard, and the third-grade program's reliance on direct dictation to the students to present the written material. Direct dictation to the students would also be used in the fourth-grade program. Worksheets were successfully eliminated from the last 40 lessons of the first-grade program during the 1978 school year (Galda et al., 1979). In this manner, the radio programs became even more economical and practically feasible to implement on a large scale. In addition, the accessibility of the radio lessons to an out-of-school listening audience was increased by not requiring any materials besides paper, pencil, and radio. The presence of such an audience was discovered in 1977 and such listeners were informally surveyed during August 1978. Results of the August survey are discussed in chapter 8.

6. THE 1978 SCHOOL YEAR

An important objective of the 1978 school year was the orderly transition from direction of project activities and administration by Stanford staff to Nicaraguan staff members. Consequently, the Nicaraguan counterparts who had been trained in the various aspects of the project were given primary responsibility for the development and production of the fourth-grade instructional program and the implementation of the first- through third-grade instructional programs. In developing the fourth-grade radio lessons, as well as in the use of the feedback system and in much of the formal evaluation, Stanford staff members served mainly in a consulting capacity.

Political Disturbances

The 1978 school year was a politically unstable year in Nicaragua. Even before the beginning of civil war in September, there were several general strikes and an atmosphere of unrest. As indicated below, however, the majority of project activities were completed as planned despite many obstacles. The office had to be closed for short periods on several occasions. The primary setback in 1978 was not to the office directly, however, but to the validity of some of the evaluation activities. This was due to the extreme irregularity of school attendance during much of the school year, especially in Masaya and Carazo.

The First- Through Fourth-grade Instructional Programs

The Radio Mathematics Project began broadcasting lessons to the first through fourth grades on February 23, 1978. During the 1978 school year, the project staff distributed materials to over 300 classrooms using project lessons. About 10,000 students in these classrooms listened to the programs. First- through third-grade radio lessons were essentially the same as those broadcast in the previous years. Fourth-grade lessons were developed during the 1978 school year with the now standard formative evaluation system.

Short teacher-training sessions (about three hours long) were conducted by project staff members for teachers in Masaya, Granada, and Carazo during early February, 1978; in Río San Juan they were conducted by the local provincial officials.

Pretests were administered to over 200 first- through fourth-grade classes in February and March, 1978. The 1978 school year ended with the posttesting of over 200 classes in the first through fourth grades in October and November, 1978. The second-grade formal evaluation was repeated to obtain further data. In addition, 24 third-grade radio classes with prior radio experience were tested to measure the cumulative effect of radio experience in successive years on mathematics achievement. This work continued the longitudinal study of the effectiveness of project lessons begun during the 1977 school year. Also, the first-grade evaluation was conducted to confirm the project's previous findings. Finally, a formal evaluation of the fourth-grade program was conducted. All of the formal evaluation activities were successfully completed despite a very tight schedule of activities and the adverse political conditions in Nicaragua in 1978. A detailed report of all formal evaluation activities is presented in chapter 4.

Río San Juan Implementation

During the 1978 school year, the Radio Mathematics Project expanded geographically beyond its experimental areas. The original experimental area in 1974–1975 covered the province of Masaya. Granada and Carazo were added in 1976. These three areas continued to receive the radio lessons in 1977 and 1978. During the second half of the 1977 school year, the project prepared to present radio lessons in Río San Juan during the 1978 school year. The expansion of the project into Río San Juan was consistent with the project's eventual goal of enabling all the school children of Nicaragua to listen to radio mathematics lessons.

A primary objective of the Río San Juan implementation was to support the successful use of the radio lessons with a minimum of assistance from the project staff after the initial training. In September 1977, a planning visit was made to Río San Juan to enlist the cooperation of local education officials and of the Río San Juan Project, a government-sponsored, integrated, rural-development program in the area. Radios for the schools in Río San Juan were purchased by the Ministry in December 1977 with the money won in the Japan Prize competition. In February 1978, several supervisors from the provincial inspectorate of education in Río San Juan spent more than a week at the Radio Mathematics Project office being trained to provide teacher training for local teachers. These supervisors distributed project materials in their local areas. Later that month, the project programs were officially used outside of the initial

experimental area for the first time. According to a report sent from
the Río San Juan Project to the Ministry of Education, the radio
mathematics lessons were among the most successful of all the activities in Río San Juan in 1978.

Dissemination Activities

The Radio Mathematics Project moved from its experimental
status to that of a well-established program during the 1978 school
year. Consequently, the number of dissemination activities conducted
by the project staff increased substantially. Project staff members
attended and presented papers at conferences in Alaska, Brazil,
Chile, Jamaica, and Washington, D.C.; visited other educational development projects in Costa Rica and the Philippines; consulted with
the staffs of other educational development projects in Nicaragua (the
Instituto de Bienestar Campesino or INVIERNO and the Rural Educational Radio Project in Puerto Cabezas, Zelaya) and the Philippines
(the RATES project) on the use of radio in education; and helped to
produce a film about the project. Several visitors, both foreign and
Nicaraguan, came to the project office. Foreign visitors included the
director of programming of Educational Television (ETV) in El Salvador. Nicaraguan visitors included several staff members of the
Rural Educational Radio Project. Plans were made to use radio mathematics programs experimentally in the Puerto Cabezas area on the
northeast coast of Nicaragua. Finally, IMSSS at Stanford published in
December 1978 a second summary volume—Suppes, Searle, and
Friend (1978)—of the activities of the Radio Mathematics Project.
This volume has been distributed to libraries throughout the United
States, England, and Canada and to individuals and organizations in
67 countries.

Other Research Activities

A primary project objective during the 1978 school year was the
completion of the many supplementary research activities conducted
by the staff. Of paramount importance to the planned wide-scale
implementation of the project was an experiment concerning the use
of worksheets in the first-grade radio lessons. Because of the cost and
distribution problems involved with the worksheets, there had been a
great deal of interest in whether the first-grade lessons could be
rewritten so as to eliminate them without sacrificing the effectiveness
of the lessons. In order to test the feasibility of this suggestion, the last
40 first-grade lessons were rewritten to eliminate the need for worksheets and were retaped. These revised lessons were played on tape
recorders in 24 experimental classrooms. Immediately before the
beginning of the experiment and immediately after the last lesson,

achievement tests were administered both to the group of students using worksheets and to the group using the revised lessons. Results of the worksheet experiment are discussed in Galda et al. (1979). The Radio Mathematics Project also cooperated with the World Bank in conducting a textbook experiment. For this experiment, free textbooks were distributed to all children in 20 first-grade and 20 fourth-grade classes. These classes were subsequently given pre- and posttests and compared with traditional classes and with classes using the radio lessons. The results of this textbook experiment will be published in the near future.

Numerous other testing activities were conducted during the 1978 school year that followed up previous project research in elementary mathematics learning. Some of these activities, like the addition-subtraction test administered in Managua, were direct offspring of earlier tests; others, like the numeration and logic tests, were new tests. A special test in mathematics was administered to fifth- and sixth-grade students. This test was designed to help the Nicaraguan staff plan the radio curriculum for those grades. Earlier project work with the Stanford Mental Arithmetic Test (SMAT), first administered at the end of the 1975 school year, was also continued; the test was given to radio classes in Grades 2 through 4, so that results could be compared with those obtained for 1976 control classes. The project also designed and administered a test of language arts to second-grade radio and control classes, to attempt to determine whether enhanced mathematics achievement in the radio classes was gained at the expense of neglecting other subject areas. For a discussion of the results of these supplementary testing activities see Galda et al. (1979) and chapter 4.

In addition to the extensive testing program described above, more research-related activities were planned. Unfortunately, not all of these could be done, because of the political situation. In late August, the project planned a series of inspection visits to all of the experimental classrooms to estimate the actual radio usage. These visits were also intended to obtain information regarding the teachers' ideas about the radio programs and related activities. Unfortunately, most of the visits had to be cancelled, because staff members were unable to visit the schools. Project staff members were able to interview children about subtraction problems, administer a questionnaire to about 100 teachers to further previous research into educational wastage (dropout and repetition problems) in the Nicaraguan educational system, and conduct an extensive informal survey of the out-of-school listening audience to estimate its magnitude and characteristics. Detailed results of these two survey studies are presented in chapters 6 and 8.

7. THE 1979 SCHOOL YEAR

Project Director Jamesine Friend left Nicaragua (to consult with a radio project in the Philippines) in the middle of the 1978 school year, and Dr. Klaus Galda, the only expatriate in the project office, took over as project director. Galda remained in Nicaragua until January 5, 1979. At that time, the Nicaraguan Ministry of Public Education assumed complete responsibility for the operation of the Radio Mathematics Project in Nicaragua. Administratively, the project was placed under the auspices of the National Center for Education and Science (Centro Nacional de Educación y Ciencias, CENEC), although for 1979 the operating funds were still being channeled through the Ministry's Office of Planning.

At the beginning of February 1979, the project office moved from Masaya to Managua where it was housed in a building that had been built for the Ministry of Public Education with AID support. Before the culmination of the civil war in June 1979, the project was occupying four large rooms (each about the size of a classroom).

The Radio Instructional Program

Lessons for Grades 2, 3, and 4 (developed in previous years) were being broadcast each morning over Radio Nacional at 8:30, 9:00, and 10:30, respectively. Since March 5, when broadcasting began, no days had been missed. However, the radio station frequently started the programs 10 to 15 minutes behind schedule.

The radio mathematics lessons were being used officially in selected schools in the provinces of Managua, Masaya, Granada, and Carazo, as well as in virtually the entire province of Río San Juan. The project staff estimated that approximately 10,000 students were listening to the radio mathematics programs in the schools that had received radios and teacher's guides. There were undoubtedly many more schools and homes listening to the programs independently. The usual three-hour training session had been given to teachers from about 30 schools in Managua, as well as to a similar number from the three provinces that had formerly made up the experimental area. Project staff members also trained six inspectors from Río San Juan, who in turn were responsible for training teachers in more than 30 schools in that province.

Pretests were administered in the second-, third-, and fourth-grade Managua classes where materials had been distributed. About 30 afternoon-shift schools were control groups in those same three grades. The purpose of pre- and posttesting in these Managua schools was to see whether the results obtained from the formal evaluation in

Masaya, Granada, and Carazo were valid for the urban Managua schools as well.

Despite a late start, work was also under way on developing the fifth-grade programs. The fourth-grade posttest was given as a pretest to 17 experimental classes. However, it appeared that there would be no formal evaluation of fifth grade in 1979, since no control group of students was selected. Of the 17 fifth-grade classes, 12 were in Managua, and the remainder were in Masaya (3 urban and 2 rural). Lesson production began about two or three weeks late, and the first fifth-grade lessons were not started until two weeks after the other grades.

The fifth-grade lessons were not broadcast but were distributed on cassette tapes to the experimental classrooms. This created a number of problems. Lessons had to be recorded almost two weeks before presentation to allow time for the reproduction and distribution of the cassette copies. Some of the tape recorders were malfunctioning and, had lessons continued, it was likely that a shortage of functioning recorders would develop. Apparently the decision to use tapes was motivated mainly by uncertainty about being able to obtain enough vehicles to observe several classrooms at exactly the same hour every day. The schools using tapes staggered their mathematics classes, so that it was possible at any hour of the morning to observe some fifth-grade class.

According to the last report received at Stanford, all of the first 12 fifth-grade lessons had been observed. Weekly testing had not begun yet but was scheduled to begin the week after Easter (the middle of April, 1979). It appeared that planning for the tests was progressing reasonably well. The master plan for the fifth grade and the curriculum seemed to be fairly complete. All these activities were subsequently overtaken by political events.

Difficulties Encountered by Nicaraguan Staff

Not surprisingly, the Nicaraguan staff members encountered several problems after the departure of the Stanford staff. A list of major problems, not necessarily in order of importance, was drawn up jointly by Galda and the Nicaraguan staff during Galda's visit to Nicaragua in March 1979. The major problems encountered by the Nicaraguan staff were in the following areas:

1. Materials and equipment—vehicles, cassette recorders, and office equipment were not maintained properly or replaced when required.
2. Curriculum—only one staff member, not an expert in curriculum, was working in this area at the time of Galda's visit.

3. Lack of direction—there was a general lack of coordination among the project activities.
4. Financial—there was a cut in the budgeted operating funds for 1979.

The Future of Instructional Radio in Nicaragua

At the time of Galda's visit in March 1979, the Radio Mathematics Project in Nicaragua was planning to expand slowly its geographic area of coverage. In addition, it was planning to serve as a model for the development of other instructional radio programs. These additional radio programs would be in other curriculum areas for primary school children, as well as for adult education, secondary education (especially in mathematics), and teacher education. A concrete result of Galda's visit was an agreement to start immediately on a publicity campaign for the Radio Mathematics programs, especially to inform schools and out-of-school listeners that the third- and fourth-grade programs could be used even if the listeners did not have the project materials. Unfortunately, the culmination of the revolution in June 1979 negated any possibility of accomplishing these objectives in 1979.[4]

8. CONCLUSIONS

The accomplishments of the Radio Mathematics Project in Nicaragua can be grouped into five classes—operational, educational, economic, organizational, and institutional.

Operational Accomplishments

The Radio Mathematics Project developed and evaluated a complete instructional program in mathematics for each of the first four primary-school grades during the tenure of Stanford involvement in Nicaragua. Despite early delays due to staffing problems, and subsequent difficulties in the transmission of the radio lessons, relationships with the Ministry, and political disturbances, the project staff maintained a brisk schedule of developing, producing, broadcasting, and evaluating radio lessons. The development and evaluation of these programs were described above and are summarized below:

---

[4] Recent correspondence from Nicaraguan staff members of the Radio Mathematics Project indicates the new government supports the work of the project and places high priority on its resumption.

Year	Grade	Development	Summative evaluation
1975	1	Lessons developed	*Nonexperimental* assessment
1976	1	Lessons revised	*Experimental* evaluation
	2	Lessons developed	*Nonexperimental* assessment
1977	2	Minor revisions	*Experimental* evaluation (posttest only)
	3	Lessons developed	*Experimental* evaluation
1978	1	1/3 lessons modified without worksheets	*Experimental* evaluation
	2		*Experimental* evaluation
	3		*Experimental* evaluation
	4	Lessons developed	*Experimental* evaluation

Educational Accomplishments

Evaluation studies of the Radio Mathematics Project's instructional program have indicated that it is educationally effective (see chap. 4). Students following the instructional radio lessons developed by the project learn more mathematics than comparable students in traditional classrooms. In addition, rural students receiving the radio lessons benefit relatively more than do urban students.

A crucial feature of the instructional system developed by the Radio Mathematics Project is a method for providing continuous information to program developers about student performance and student and teacher reaction to all aspects of the program as mandated in the original contract. The project devised a system for using feedback that allowed the development of a full course of radio lessons within one school year. The unique feature of this system is that old lessons are *not* revised; rather, new lessons are designed to build on the learning that has already occurred—if necessary, changing time allotments for different topics and modifying the strategies used. In this manner, the Radio Mathematics Project makes formative, ongoing evaluation an integral part of lesson production. The project staff considers the fast-feedback system a major contributor to the effectiveness of project lessons. (A complete description of the formative evaluation system devised and used by the Radio Mathematics Project is provided in chap. 3.)

Success of the Radio Mathematics Project lessons required the cooperation of the classroom teachers. It was therefore important that teachers perceive the program as valid and appropriately meeting the needs and engaging the attention of the students. Surveys indicated that teachers participating in the Radio Mathematics Project have quite favorable attitudes toward radio instruction. Specifically, they felt that the radio lessons help the children learn mathematics, help the teachers teach mathematics, motivate the children and make the class more interesting, and make mathematics easier for the children to learn and for the teachers to teach. More significantly, teachers not using the radio lessons agreed with those who did that the lessons would motivate the children and make the classes more interesting. In addition, they expressed an eagerness to participate in the project—a subtle measure of the project's success that should not be underestimated.

Economic Accomplishments

A heavy initial financial investment in development enabled the project to succeed in producing courses of instruction that are highly effective (as demonstrated by evaluation data), require a minimum of materials beyond the radio in the classroom, and are well accepted by teachers and students. The project's method of lesson development with formative evaluation requires a large staff to design and administer weekly achievement tests and to conduct daily classroom observations. Consequently, the curriculum development process is quite expensive (Wells & Klees, 1978). However, this is only an initial cost, since the taped programs can be used for several years. In addition, the development of a final set of lessons for a grade within one school year (in contrast to the two years needed when lessons are revised) limits the substantial curriculum development costs incurred at the inception of the project to one year for each grade. Finally, because the project had a research focus, and was engaged in developing new methods, the audience was kept relatively small (3,000 to 4,000 students per year at the outset of the project). In subsequent implementations, the per-student costs for lesson development would be smaller if the program were designed to reach a larger audience from the start.

An explicit goal of the project was to minimize implementation costs (i.e., the recurring operational cost of using the programs once they are developed). The project requires only a low level of teacher training—about three hours per year—and no supervision. A minimum of supporting materials is necessary in the classroom—a teacher's guide, some simple materials (most of which can be collected locally at no cost), a few posters, and other materials. Only the first-grade lessons require student worksheets, and in 1978 one-third of the lessons were rewritten to be independent of worksheets. Besides keeping the amount of necessary supporting materials to a minimum, the project made no special investment in communications infrastructure beyond purchasing radio receivers. The project used existing recording and transmitting facilities. The first priority was the development of effective software. Thus, recurring operational costs were low; the logic was to invest heavily in developing effective, stand-alone lessons that could be used easily and cheaply in the field.

Organizational and Institutional Accomplishments

When the Radio Mathematics Project opened its office in Nicaragua in 1974, there had never been a media-based instructional program in the country. In fact, there had been no indigenous radio or TV programming for children. The mathematics curriculum department of the Ministry of Education consisted of two people (both of whom immediately joined the project staff). When the last Stanford staff member left in December 1978, an operational staff of 30 people was left behind that was able to continue the developmental work as well as to oversee the broadcasting of lessons to more than 10,000 students daily. Until political events overtook them, the staff continued developing lessons for the fifth grade, producing over 50 lesson tapes and teacher's guides.

An important organizational characteristic of the Radio Mathematics Project was its semiautonomy from the educational bureaucracy of Nicaragua. Both financial and administrative control of day-to-day matters were entirely in the hands of the project director. This was an important factor in the project's ability to maintain a demanding production schedule. It would have been impossible to consult with the Ministry on all decisions and remain on schedule. Several factors contributed to the relative freedom with which the project operated: the circumstances under which the project came to Nicaragua, the nature of the agreement between AID and the Nicaraguan government, the physical separation of the Ministry and the project office, and the continuing effort of the project director to maintain the project's autonomy.

As the first extensive research-and-development educational project in Nicaragua, the Radio Mathematics Project established an atmosphere conducive to successful educational innovation and improvement. Through the training and experience offered to Nicaraguan staff members of the project, it created a competent educational research staff and tradition in a setting where such had not existed before. These individuals are capable of continuing and extending the success of the project without expatriate technical assistance.

Summary

The success of the Radio Mathematics Project has taken an enormous effort on the part of many people and has involved many different factors. First, the project was given long-term funding to carry out a project with clear research aims. The research focus of the project was entirely appropriate, since it was attempting something that had not been done before. A radio-instructional project adopting our program as a model would not need such a strong research component. However, there are many unsolved problems in education, and other new ideas will need to be experimented with. It is important that such new projects have enough time and resources to give the new ideas a fair trial.

Second, although the project had its differences and difficulties with the Nicaraguan Ministry of Education, the support the Ministry provided throughout the life of the project was an important component of its success. They did not interfere in the internal affairs of the project but did provide a substantial amount of material support.

Finally, good organizational techniques, clear lines of authority, and adequate resources may be prerequisites to success, but they cannot substitute for interest, dedication, and ingenuity on the part of people who are working together to meet project goals. The Radio Mathematics Project was fortunate enough to attract individuals with these qualities.

REFERENCES

Friend, J. *Closing the feedback loop.* Paper presented at the international conference: The Use of Radio as an Instructional Tool in Primary Schools. Managua, Nicaragua, September 1976. (a)

Friend, J. *The flexible master plan.* Paper presented at the international conference: The Use of Radio as an Instructional Tool in Primary Schools. Managua, Nicaragua, September 1976. (b)

Friend, J. *Planning for change.* Paper presented at the international conference: The Use of Radio as an Instructional Tool in Primary Schools. Managua, Nicaragua, September 1976. (c)

Friend, J. *Column addition skills.* Paper presented at the American Educational Research Association Convention, San Francisco, April 1979.

Galda, K., & de Quintanilla, A. Weekly tests. In P. Suppes, B. Searle, & J. Friend (Eds.), *The Radio Mathematics Project: Nicaragua, 1976–1977.* Stanford, Calif.: Stanford University, Institute for Mathematical Studies in the Social Sciences, 1978.

Galda, K., González, J., Searle, B., & Friend, J. *Application of radio to teaching elementary mathematics in a developing country* (6th annual report). Stanford, Calif.: Stanford University, Institute for Mathematical Studies in the Social Sciences, 1979.

Jamison, D.   Radio education and student repetition in Nicaragua. In
   P. Suppes, B. Searle, & J. Friend (Eds.),   *The Radio Mathematics Project:
   Nicaragua, 1976–1977.* Stanford, Calif.: Stanford University, Institute for
   Mathematical Studies in the Social Sciences, 1978.

Searle, B.   *Application of radio to teaching elementary mathematics in a developing
   country* (1st annual report). Stanford, Calif.: Stanford University, Institute
   for Mathematical Studies in the Social Sciences, 1974. (a)

Searle, B.   *Site selection process: Radio Mathematics Project.* Stanford, Calif.:
   Stanford University, Institute for Mathematical Studies in the Social Sciences, 1974. (b)

Searle, B.   The impact of project goals on organization: A case study of the
   Nicaragua Radio Mathematics Project.   In *The organization and management
   of educational distance media systems: Some new directions* (A UNESCO Report,
   contract numbers 506–649 and 506–824). Palo Alto, Calif.: EDUTEL
   Communications and Development, Inc., 1979.

Searle, B., Friend, J., & Suppes, P.   *Application of radio to teaching elementary
   mathematics in a developing country* (2nd annual report). Stanford, Calif.:
   Stanford University, Institute for Mathematical Studies in the Social Sciences, 1975.

Searle, B., Friend, J., & Suppes, P.   *The Radio Mathematics Project: Nicaragua,
   1974–1975.* Stanford, Calif.: Stanford University, Institute for Mathematical Studies in the Social Sciences, 1976.

Searle, B., Friend, J., Suppes, P., & Tilson, T.   *Application of radio to teaching
   elementary mathematics in a developing country* (4th annual report). Stanford,
   Calif.: Stanford University, Institute for Mathematical Studies in the Social
   Sciences, 1977.

Searle, B., & González, J.   *Teaching mathematics by radio: A project to improve the
   quality of primary school education.* Unpublished manuscript, Stanford University, Institute for Mathematical Studies in the Social Sciences, 1979.

Searle, B., Matthews, P., Suppes, P., & Friend, J.   Formal evaluation of the
   1976 first-grade instructional program. In P. Suppes, B. Searle, &
   J. Friend (Eds.),   *The Radio Mathematics Project: Nicaragua, 1976–1977.*
   Stanford, Calif.: Stanford University, Institute for Mathematical Studies in
   the Social Sciences, 1978.

Suppes, P., Searle, B., & Friend, J. (Eds.).   *The Radio Mathematics Project:
   Nicaragua, 1976–1977.* Stanford, Calif.: Stanford University, Institute for
   Mathematical Studies in the Social Sciences, 1978.

Tilson, T., & Searle, B.   An assessment of teacher attitudes. In P. Suppes,
   B. Searle, & J. Friend (Eds.),   *The Radio Mathematics Project: Nicaragua,
   1976–1977.* Stanford, Calif.: Stanford University, Institute for Mathematical Studies in the Social Sciences, 1978.

Tilson, T., Searle, B., Friend, J., & Suppes, P.   *Application of radio to teaching
   elementary mathematics in a developing country* (5th annual report). Stanford,
   Calif.: Stanford University, Institute for Mathematical Studies in the Social
   Sciences, 1978.

Wells, S., & Klees, S.   Education decisions and cost analysis for the Radio
   Mathematics Project in Nicaragua. In P. Suppes, B. Searle, & J. Friend
   (Eds.), *The Radio Mathematics Project: Nicaragua, 1976–1977.* Stanford,
   Calif.: Stanford University, Institute for Mathematical Studies in the Social
   Sciences, 1978.

APPENDIX A

CHRONOLOGY OF THE RADIO MATHEMATICS PROJECT
(July 1, 1973 to June 30, 1979)

1973

July 1	Initial contract period begins
September 5–19	Site-selection trip to Southeast Asia
November 8–20	Site-selection trip to Latin America

1974

January 6–21	Site-selection trip to Latin America and Africa
February 1	**Project Director Jamesine Friend hired**
February 8	Site selection meeting with AID officials held in Washington, D.C.
	Report on trips, "Site Selection Process: Radio Mathematics Project" distributed
February 11	Nicaragua selected as first choice for project site
March 6–15	Staff visit to Nicaragua for further negotiations
April 1	Agreement between AID and Nicaragua formalized
April 1–May 10	AID orientation and language training for Stanford staff who were moving to Nicaragua

June 1	Radio specialist hired
June 9–25	Arrival of Stanford staff in Nicaragua
June 21	Project Research Review Committee meeting
July 4	Office opened in Masaya, Nicaragua
September 3–November 13	Six lessons pilot-tested
October 22–November 15	Achievement test administered to 44 first-grade classes
	Attitude questionnaire given to 44 first-grade teachers

1975

February 10, 13, 20, 29	Weekly teacher-training sessions
February 12	First day of 1975 school year
February 24	Project mathematics lessons started in 16 experimental classes
March 3–7	Mathematics pretest administered in 16 experimental classes
March 6	Teacher-training session
April 7–11	Mathematics pretest administered in 9 additional classes
April 10	Teacher-training session
May 12	Experimental lessons started in 6 Granada schools

June 19	Teacher-training session
June 30	Lesson 70 for first grade presented in experimental classrooms
July 1	Middle of 1975 school year
	Lesson 71 for first grade presented in experimental classrooms
August 6	Weekly paper-and-pencil tests initiated
September-November	Mental arithmetic tests administered
October 27–November 14	**Posttests administered to first and second grades**
	Teacher questionnaires distributed
	Teacher interviews conducted
November 21	End of school year
	Lesson 150 for first grade presented in experimental classrooms

1976

January 14	Research Committee meeting at Stanford
February 9–13	First teacher-training sessions held
February 16	Lesson 1 for first grade (8:30 A.M.) and Lesson 1 for **second grade (9:45 A.M.)** broadcast over Radio Nacional

February 23–March 29   Pretests administered in first grade

March   Teacher questionnaires distributed

March 3–April 2   Pretests administered in second grade

March 12–April 7   Pretests administered in third grade

March 15–19   Second teacher-training sessions held

April 2–7   Pretests administered in fourth grade

June 30   Lesson 89 for first and second grades broadcast over Radio Nacional

July 1   Middle of 1976 school year

Lesson 90 broadcast by Radio Nacional to 45 first-grade and 40 second-grade classes in Masaya, Granada, and Carazo

Weekly test administration continued in 12 first-grade and 12 second-grade classes

August 4   **Presentation by Nicaraguan staff members to school inspectors and subinspectors**

August 16–30   Addition and subtraction test administered to 2,000 students, in first through fourth grades in Managua

September 5–10   International conference on instructional radio held at INCAE, Managua

September 20–28	Addition and subtraction test administered to 1,000 students, in fifth and sixth grades in Managua
October 11–November 12	Posttests administered to 53 first-grade, 46 second-grade, 24 third-grade, and 12 fourth-grade classes
	Questionnaires administered to teachers
	Forms sent to teachers for collection of student data
October 13	Lesson 150 broadcast (last first-grade lesson)
October 14	Lesson 1 of second grade broadcast to first grade
November 1	*The Radio Mathematics Project: Nicaragua 1974–1975* published
November 18	Last day of regular classes
	Lesson 25 of second grade broadcast to first grade
	Lesson 175 broadcast to second grade
December 1–2	Seminar on Radio Mathematics Project held in Masaya for Ministry of Public Education and university personnel

1977

January 24–26	Field visit, sponsored by EDUTEL, for economic study of the project
February 15–19	Teacher training, one session each for participating teachers in Masaya, Granada, and Carazo
February 28	Lesson 1 broadcast by Radio Nacional to 55 second-grade classes and 60 third-grade classes
February 28–March 17	Pretests administered to 18 second-grade, 36 third-grade, and 24 fourth-grade classes
March 1	Japan Prize awarded to the Radio Mathematics Project for Lesson 171, second grade
March 10	AID review meeting in Washington, D.C.
April	Forms sent to teachers for collection of student data
June 22	AID and Ministry of Public Education sign new contract to extend project
June 30	Middle of 1977 school year
	Lesson 79 broadcast to second and third grades
	End of initial four-year contract
July	Children interviewed on working subtraction exercises

July 1	Continuation contract starting date
September	Visit to Río San Juan to plan for 1978 implementation
September 28–October 14	Unannounced visits to schools using radio lessons
November	Listener survey conducted
November 9	End of posttesting second, third, and fourth grades
November 18	Lesson 164 broadcast to second and third grades
December	Ministry of Public Education purchased 43 radios with money received from Japan Prize
December 10–13	Staff members visited Instituto Costarricense de Enseñanza Radiofónica (ICER)

1978

January 20–30	Training for school inspectors from Río San Juan
February 15–17	Teacher training for Masaya, Granada, and Carazo
February 17–March 1	Vitalia Rojas at conference in Brazil
February 21–March 15	Pretests administered to over 200 classrooms in first through fourth grades
February 23	**Broadcast of project lessons for first through fourth grades begun**

April 6–13	Training for INVIERNO staff
April 25–May 3	Footage shot for project film by Metrotone
May 20–29	Juan José Montenegro at conference "Transfer of Technology in Education," Vina del Mar, Chile
June 15–October 15	Jamesine Friend in Philippines at RATES project
June 28–July 1	Barbara Searle participates in Seminar in Radio Education, Caribbean Region, Ocho Ríos, Jamaica
July–September	Mental arithmetic tests administered in radio classes, second through fourth grades
July 1–7	Visit from director of programming, ETV El Salvador
July 3–10	Addition and subtraction test administered in Managua
July 25	Visit from Puerto Cabezas Wisconsin Project
August 1–3	Listener survey conducted
August 2–11	Numeration test administered in Managua to first through sixth grades
August 12	Training for teachers using new first-grade lessons
August 14–21	**Pretest for worksheet experiment administered in 48 classes**

August 14–28	Logic test in Managua and experimental area
August 16–18	Barbara Searle at the Audio Conference of "Educational Telecommunications for Alaska," sponsored by the Northwest Regional Educational Laboratory
August 18	New first-grade lessons (without worksheets) with cassettes begun in 24 classrooms
August 28–31	Classroom inspection visits begun
October 3–November 9	Posttesting of over 200 classes, first through fourth grades
October 9–11	Special test given to 40 fifth- and sixth-grade classes
October 13–31	Spanish test given to 40 second-grade classes
October 21	Teachers' questionnaire on promotion given to 96 teachers
November 16–20	Klaus Galda at Puerto Cabezas Wisconsin project
December	*The Radio Mathematics Project: Nicaragua 1976–1977* published

1979

| January 5 | Stanford participation in Nicaragua ended |

February 10–13	Klaus Galda at 5th Interamerican Conference on Mathematical Education at Campinas, Brazil
March 18–28	Follow-up visit to Nicaragua by Klaus Galda
June 1–7	**Klaus Galda at Conference on Communications in Development, Jamaica**
June 29	Project film shown at Workshop on Communications in Rural Development, Washington, D.C.

This chapter discusses the multitudinous factors that shaped the curriculum produced by the Radio Mathematics Project. The interplay of these factors—some of which were idealistic or philosophical, others more practical—resulted in a series of radio programs quite uncharacteristic of what one ordinarily thinks of as educational broadcasting. There were no lectures; the programs were more a dialogue between teacher and child, with the children taking a larger part than is usual in such transactions. The programs were not supplementary to the regular course of instruction but completely replaced the regular curriculum. The postbroadcast activities were integrated in such a way that the radio teachers and the classroom teacher formed a well-coordinated teaching team.

In a typical classroom, the teacher starts the daily lesson a few minutes before broadcast time by handing out materials that will be required during the broadcast. She then turns on the radio and allows the radio teachers to take over. During the broadcast, the classroom teacher will not be needed except to maintain discipline. If she has another grade in the same classroom, she can devote the next half hour to them. Otherwise, she may provide special help for individual students, especially in first grade. During the broadcast, the radio teachers talk directly to the children in the classroom, giving instructions, leading group songs, asking questions, explaining mathematical concepts, introducing dramatized problem situations, telling jokes, and so on. Whenever a radio teacher gives an instruction or asks a question, there is a pause so that the children in the classroom can respond. Most of the children's responses are oral, but they may also be asked to solve written arithmetic exercises according to the directions given by the radio teachers, to make drawings in their notebooks, to write numbers from dictation, or to count seeds or stones that they have brought to class for that purpose. They may sing, guess the answers to riddles, or recite poems. The lessons are fast paced, with frequent changes of topic. Discussions of mathematical concepts are mixed with short sessions of rote drill and spiced with frequent "entertainment" breaks. There are four to seven different mathematical segments in each lesson, covering a wide range of topics so that the children are continuously reviewing old material as well as learning new skills and concepts. Children are encouraged to participate actively in both the instructional segments and the entertainment breaks. Although radio is a one-way medium of communication, the conversational tone, the appropriateness of the language, and the carefully controlled pace produce the impression of two-way communication between the radio personalities and the students in the classroom.

Because the radio teachers set the pace, and essentially take over the classroom during the broadcast period, there is little variation between classrooms during this part of the mathematics lessons. Urban classrooms of 30 to 50 children behave very much like rural classrooms of fewer than 15 children. The main difference between classrooms comes in the postbroadcast session, when the classroom teacher again takes charge. Within the broad constraints of the suggestions supplied by the teacher's guide, the classroom teacher is now free to adapt the activities to the special needs of the children in the class. The suggested postbroadcast activities usually allow for more interaction between children than can be allowed during the broadcast. There is also more leeway for interactions between the teacher and individual children.

During the postbroadcast portion of the lesson, the scene is very much like that in any traditional classroom. The teacher explains and gives examples, allowing individual children to ask questions or to contribute in other ways to a "conversation" that involves the entire class. Then individual or small-group assignments are given, and the children work semiautonomously as the teacher circulates in the classroom giving special instruction where needed. During the postbroadcast period, not all children work at the same rate, or even on the same tasks. The tone is generally more relaxed than during the radio part of the lesson, with less pressure to keep up the pace and with more time for following sidetracks.

Chapter 2

SHAPING THE
RADIO MATHEMATICS CURRICULUM

JAMESINE FRIEND

THE MAIN GOAL of the Radio Mathematics Project was to improve the quality of the mathematics instruction offered to children in Nicaraguan public primary schools. The terms of the contracts between AID and Stanford University, and between the U.S. and Nicaraguan governments, specified this goal and imposed some constraints as well: Radio was to be used as the primary medium of instruction and the instruction was to be delivered at a low cost.

Besides these two major constraints, there were numerous minor constraints, some explicitly stated in the contracts or in applicable public laws, others implicit in the contracts or in the characteristics of the society in which the project was to be located. We were constrained, for example, to implement the official syllabus for the mathematics curriculum. We had to work within the infrastructural limitations of the country, and within the confines of the cultural milieu. We could not select the audience—the programs were to be aimed at all public-school children, including the rural poor—so we had to cope with the limitations of the Nicaraguan school children, their teachers, and their schools, whatever those limitations might be. In the end it was the constraints as well as the goals that gave the curriculum its shape, and it is within this framework that we discuss the various aspects of the curriculum design.

The first section of this chapter describes the instructional package prepared by the project—a series of radio programs together with the supporting materials needed to form a complete mathematics curriculum. The next section discusses the pedagogical goals of the curriculum design. We then turn, in the third section, to a rather extensive examination of the constraints and their effects. A final section provides a summary.

1. THE CURRICULUM PACKAGE

During the four and a half years that Stanford was involved in the Radio Mathematics Project in Nicaragua, complete curriculum packages for the first through the fourth grades were developed. (The project is presently continuing under the auspices of the Nicaraguan government, and additional curriculum materials have been developed since the departure of the Stanford advisors.) The curriculum for each grade consisted of a series of radio lessons, a plan for postbroadcast activities (delivered to the teachers in the form of a teacher's guide for the grade), and a set of materials to be used in teacher training. At some grade levels, supplementary printed materials for the children were provided.

The number of radio programs in each series varied somewhat from year to year. Although there are, by law, 180 school days in the school year, we found that it was not feasible to broadcast more than 165 lessons per year because of frequent holidays, days taken in final testing, and occasional preemptions of the transmitter for various (usually political) purposes. The length of the daily radio programs varied somewhat at the beginning, but we soon standardized our programs to fit into the conventional half-hour broadcasting slot. The total time that the children can devote daily to mathematics is determined by a Ministry of Education ruling that specifies 80 minutes per day. (In practice, we found that teachers allowed between 40 and 60 minutes per day, depending on grade level.) For each grade, the time that was left after the radio broadcast had ended was used for postbroadcast activities designed to supplement the radio programs.

The supplementary printed materials for the children varied greatly from grade to grade, with a strong trend toward the complete elimination of such materials. In first grade there were individual student worksheets for the majority of the lessons; subsequently, the first grade series was revised to eliminate worksheets in the last third of the course. In second grade, no individual worksheets were used, but a set of 14 posters was supplied to each class to illustrate the concepts of area and fractions. In third and fourth grades, only pasteboard rulers and inexpensive copies of the multiplication and division tables were supplied; there were no posters or other materials for group use.

The teacher's guides were bound books of from 200 to 250 pages. On one page for each lesson, specific suggestions were given for activities before, during, and after the broadcasts. In addition, the guides provided brief introductions, and included some appendices with suggestions for special activities like mathematical games.

Because teacher training consisted of only a single 3-hour session at the beginning of the school year, training materials were minimal: a brief handout that summarized the important points about using the program and a broadcast schedule for the year.

2. GOALS OF THE CURRICULUM DESIGN

The predominant concern of the curriculum designers was always the basic goal of increasing the children's mathematical skills and knowledge. The majority of the curriculum decisions hinged on trade-offs between this goal and one or another of the numerous constraints on it. To realize the primary goal of increased achievement, we tried to accomplish a number of pedagogical subgoals that we felt were necessary for an effective instructional system. Most of these are general goals that apply to all skill areas; others are more specific to the teaching of mathematics.

The first of the general goals was to gain the active participation of the students in the learning process. Children do not learn well from instruction delivered in the form of lectures or lengthy explanations. Skills and detailed factual knowledge, which play a large part in arithmetic, are particularly difficult to transmit without active participation of the children.

The second goal—always informing students of correct answers to exercises—is based on the principle that knowlege of errors makes learning more efficient.

Our third goal was to include sufficient review of basic concepts, and sufficient practice of skills and facts. This review should be well distributed over time rather than supplied as massive doses of instruction without follow-up, since distributed practice leads to better long-term retention of information. Concepts should be developed gradually, with adequate examples, because children ordinarily learn better from relevant examples than from highly verbal explanations of underlying principles, and they need time to internalize the concepts being conveyed.

In mathematics, specifically, the sequence of instruction needs to be planned correctly so that each new step builds on previous knowledge. Children cannot learn topics for which they do not have the necessary prerequisite knowledge. The correct sequencing of topics is probably more important in mathematics than in any other school subject.

3. FACTORS CONSTRAINING CURRICULUM DESIGN

Of the conditions that shaped the design of the curriculum, the most influential were the use of radio as the medium of instruction and the contractual restrictions on costs.

We begin our discussion of limiting factors with these two. We then discuss the constraints imposed by the use of formative evaluation, by Ministry guidelines for the content of the mathematics curriculum, by limitations of the Nicaraguan school environment itself, by the background of the teachers and certain characteristics of the students, and by various logistic problems.

In the following, although we discuss each factor as a constraint on curriculum planning, it is important to note that there were sometimes advantages as well as disadvantages to the limitations imposed. We identify radio, for example, as constraining curriculum design. In our view, any medium of instruction has limitations that must be taken into account in the curriculum design, and radio is not the worst of all possibilities. In fact, in many ways, as we shall point out, the advantages of radio are substantial, and not simply from the viewpoint of the costs involved.

We also discuss the *limitations* of the teachers. While it is true that the Nicaraguan educational system would be better if the teachers were better trained (and better paid), it is also true that they were marvelously pleasant, cooperative, open-minded, and clearly an asset rather than a liability.

There were instances when we felt that we had compromised our goals because of some limitation that we could not circumvent, yet it turned out that the compromise position led to better instruction than we might have developed otherwise. Several examples of this are mentioned in the following discussion.

Most of the constraints were not rigid, and some were not even well defined. Although we were to use radio as the *primary* medium of instruction, we could and did use supplements. Restrictions on costs were among the most poorly defined of the constraints on our program; there were no clear guidelines for optimal costs, and even our cost estimates were questionable. Language constraints, likewise, were poorly defined; different informants gave us widely different opinions of the prevalence, comprehensibility, and acceptability of proposed language patterns.

As a result, we frequently treated the constraints flexibly. If we felt that conforming to a questionable or poorly defined restriction would do irreparable harm to the integrity of the curriculum package, we violated the restriction rather than adapt the instructional design to it.

Radio as the Medium of Instruction

Before the Radio Mathematics Project began producing lessons, many people expressed doubts that radio could be used to teach mathematics; radio could perhaps be used to teach language or music or social studies, but for a subject as difficult to teach as mathematics, the constraints would prove too great. Most of these comments came from people who felt that television would be a more appropriate medium; apparently they perceived the main limitation of radio to be that it provides only oral communication. While it is true that the absence of a visual component is troublesome, oral communication itself has many advantages that are not shared by media such as textbooks and film strips. And two of the major limitations of radio are also shared by television—they are both mass media and they both provide only one-way communication.

Thus, there are four characteristics of radio that have an impact on curriculum. Radio

1. communicates orally,

2. does not have a visual component,

3. is a mass medium, and

4. allows only one-way communication.

The first of these characteristics is mostly advantageous; the others have some advantages but are primarily disadvantageous.

Oral communication. Language is our primary means of sharing knowledge and preserving culture. Although print has been a tremendous force in improving communication and the speed with which ideas are transmitted and changed, even in the most highly developed countries we still communicate primarily by spoken rather than written language. In less developed countries, where literacy is less common, spoken language is even more important, and among the children of any nation, oral skills are always much more highly developed than reading skills. Good communication with a not-yet-literate audience must have an oral component. Radio is one way—and the cheapest way—to provide this.

Knowing that the primary means of communication with the children will be oral shapes the thinking of the curriculum designer in many ways, both about course content and about pedagogical style.

In deciding the objectives for each year's curriculum, we put more emphasis on mental arithmetic than most traditional curriculums would, because we wanted to take advantage of the oral channel of communication and because we felt that facility with mental computations is greatly needed in a culture that is primarily oral. We saw mental arithmetic not only as a legitimate goal in itself but also as a substitute for activities that are usually based on print, for example, drill on addition and multiplication tables.

Because oral expression is learned before reading and is more natural, we saw oral work on most topics as prerequisite to printed work. Addition in first grade, for example, was taught first orally, so that the children were able to respond easily to items like 3 + 4, 5 + 1, and 7 − 2 in oral form before they were shown the printed versions of these same exercises. Similarly, fractions were taught first in oral form. In fact, with fractions, the difference between the oral and printed forms is great, and it is not unusual to find children in the early grades who understand elementary fraction concepts quite well without being able either to read or to write the numbers in the conventional fraction form. Even in integer numeration, the spoken words for numbers are more natural and more easily learned than the written forms. One of the greatest difficulties in learning to read and write numbers is with numbers that use zeros as placeholders, for instance, 203, 40, 7005, and 6050; in oral form these numbers are as easy to understand as 243, 42, 7165, and 6253.

One of the most difficult parts of elementary mathematics to teach is solving word problems. These problems are traditionally given in concise, printed form: "Mrs. Jones has three children. She gives each of them . . ." Such problems cause great difficulty for most children, and although we do not have a complete understanding of the cognitive skills employed in solving such problems, we expected to be able to circumvent the difficulty attributed to insufficient reading skills by giving the problems orally. Another hypothesis about why children do poorly with word problems is that the statements of such problems are excessively terse without any of the surrounding details that could enable the children to form a mental image of the problem situation. One reason problems are stated so briefly in textbooks is, of course, to minimize the reading demands. With an oral medium we had no such constraint but were free to supply as much detail as necessary to flesh out the story.

For many word problems, we used a complete dramatization with realistic character portrayals and plots with tension, climax, and resolution. Music and a large variety of sound effects, some recorded locally, were used liberally. These minidramas were usually no more than three or four minutes long, so as not to strain the attention span of our audience. We frequently used a series of related story problems, the first of which would be given as a full-blown dramatization while the others were more sketchy, relying on the children to imagine the details necessary to complete the picture of the situation.

Absence of visual component. We exploited the oral aspect of radio whenever possible. However, the fact that radio provides *only* oral communication poses problems for teaching mathematics. Much of mathematics is visual, especially during early stages of learning. Most of geometry deals with shapes and the relationships among them. Similarly, measurement is concerned with visual objects—with rulers and things to be measured, with containers for liquids, with surfaces and solids. Even time and weight, which are not themselves visual, are measured by instruments that are read visually. Arithmetic, except for a few simple computations that can be done mentally, deals with written or printed numbers and exercises.

Since radio cannot provide visual displays, we had to resort to other means of providing them or find other ways to teach the topic if we could. We used as substitutes a variety of media: worksheets, children's fingers, chalkboards, exercises copied into notebooks from chalkboards or from dictation, posters, and pictures drawn by the children.

Most of these are static displays, unlike the moving illustrations that film or television can provide. In most cases, we found the substitutes to be reasonably satisfactory, but sometimes the constraints imposed by an oral medium with static visual material were severe. A case in point was in the teaching of the sequence of steps that make up the arithmetic algorithms. In an algorithm like long division, for example, there is a great deal of moving from one place to another, looking first at a number here, then one there, writing a number in one place, then writing a different number obtained by a different process in another place. The sequence in which these actions are performed is very strict; any deviation will produce an incorrect answer. Because the algorithm is complex, it is not easily learned; children must see many demonstrations of the correct sequence before they can mimic it successfully. In a traditional classroom, the teacher will demonstrate the procedure on the chalkboard, taking it one step at a time and carefully explaining each step as it occurs. In this way, the children see the algorithm unfold dynamically. They do not need to study a complete solution and try to imagine the appearance of the display as it was developed.

With radio, such a dynamic display could be done with the help of the classroom teacher, who could give a demonstration synchronized with the instructions given by a radio teacher. We chose not to adopt this solution because we wanted to leave the teacher free to attend to other groups of children and because we anticipated the possibility of students working without the help of a teacher.

The solution we chose instead—and it turned out to have unexpected benefits—was to ask the children to give themselves their own demonstrations. That is, we did not ask one child to demonstrate for the class much as a teacher might; rather, we gave sufficient instructions for each child to produce in his own notebook a step-by-step demonstration of the correct process. (If one thinks of the complexity of giving instructions for long division that are so precise that a person who has never seen the process can produce a correct solution, the idea may be appalling. Rest assured that we did not start with long division; we—the curriculum writers—had had ample practice with writing instructions to work through the simpler algorithms before we reached long division.) The unexpected benefit of this substitute for moving illustrations was that the children attended more closely and learned more quickly than do children watching a demonstration given by someone else. This seems obvious now but did not occur to us before the fact.

Radio as a mass medium. Radio delivers the same message simultaneously to many listeners and therefore does not permit the individualization of instruction. In this respect, radio is even more constrained than the traditional lecture style of instruction; a lecturer can at least adjust the pace of his presentation to the needs of those to whom he is lecturing. In contrast, radio delivers the same message to small rural classes as to large urban classes. Classes in middle-class neighborhoods will be treated the same as classes of the children of poor farm laborers.

There are very few ways to alleviate this problem. One partial solution would be to prepare for each grade several series of programs at different levels. We did not seriously entertain this notion because of the prohibitive cost. Another possibility—one that we did experiment with—was to include instruction at different levels within the same broadcast. We used two levels—not for the entire lesson but only for selected parts. The exercises for the two levels were intermixed so that one ability group could be completing an exercise while another group was receiving instructions. The children adapted more easily to this style of instruction than we expected, but we abandoned the experiment after a few weeks—for two reasons. The first was that both groups were receiving less total instruction than they would have if there had been a program designed especially for them. We felt that this loss of time nearly cancelled the advantage of having the instruction aimed more nearly at the right level. The second reason for giving up this idea was the difficulty of sorting the children correctly into the two ability groups. With adequate research and a good pretesting program we probably could have overcome this difficulty, but we estimated the cost of the solution to be greater than its value. Even had this solution proved feasible, the resulting instruction would still not have approached individualization. In the end, we simply accepted the fact that radio is a mass medium and aimed our programs at, or a little below, the level of an average student.

Despite our misgivings, the level of difficulty we adopted proved quite acceptable. We had fears that by aiming at the average student we would be seriously handicapping both the above-average and the below-average students, but evaluation results showed that children of all ability levels learned substantially more than comparable students in traditional classrooms (see chap. 4).

A mass medium also offers some advantages. Since the curriculum is centrally controlled, there can be more consistency than would be possible with media like textbooks that allow for greater classroom variation. Because financial support can be concentrated in this case, more time and care can be spent planning the curriculum and fitting it to the special needs of the audience.

One-way communication. Radio provides communication in one direction only. This characteristic is so much a part of our perception of radio as a communication medium that many producers do not even see it as a problem to be overcome. Most radio programs are clearly designed with only one-way communication in mind; the radio talks (or makes some other noises) continuously, and that is seen as so right and proper that professional radio people are appalled at the thought of "dead air." This deep-seated prejudice was evident among project staff members; most of the scriptwriters, especially at the beginning, tended to think far more about what the radio would be doing than about what the students would be doing. This attitude was frequently counterproductive, since our aim was not to produce radio programs but to educate children, which we felt we could do best by allowing them time to participate rather than by demanding that they listen continuously.

Since our focus was more on the learner than on the radio, we developed a style that closely simulated a conversation between student and teacher. The radio characters spoke directly to the children rather than to one another. They gave instructions and asked questions and always paused to allow the children time to do the task or to answer. Only rarely did more than two or three minutes elapse without an opportunity for the children to engage in some activity.

For the programs to simulate dialogue between radio teachers and classroom students, the pauses for responses and other activities had to be calculated quite precisely. If a pause is too short, the children will not be able to complete the activity in the time allotted and will not be paying attention to the next instruction or question. With oral responses they will not even hear the next radio speech, since a choral response from an entire class is loud enough to drown out the radio. If the pause is too long, the children will become restless and may distract one another so that again they are not listening to the next question or instruction from the radio teacher.

We found no theoretical approach to calculating appropriate lengths for pauses, but we did develop quite complete rules of thumb simply by observing large numbers of children making many responses of different kinds. One difficulty in choosing pause lengths is that the speed with which children respond changes quite dramatically as they gain experience. By the end of second grade, for example, children can write a three-digit number from dictation in 8 seconds, whereas at the beginning of the same grade they needed 12 seconds—if they could do it at all.

There is usually little difficulty in teaching children to participate actively in the kind of simulated conversations we prepared. In the first few lessons of each year, we encouraged the children with phrases such as "Now, everyone answer this one aloud" and "I want to hear all of you tell me the answer." For many lessons we also used child actors to provide an example and stimulus for the children in the classroom. These child actors, usually three or four of them, responded to each question asked by the radio teachers in the same way we wanted the children in the classroom to respond, thereby setting the pace for any children who were at all hesitant. We also asked the classroom teachers to encourage active participation; the best way for them to do this is to participate along with the class, giving answers aloud just as they expect the children to do.

Even though we succeeded in simulating a dialogue, we still had the problem of not really receiving any communication from the audience. The radio could begin a conversation by giving an instruction or asking a question, and it could then pause so the children could respond, but it could not continue on to the next stage of a real conversation by reacting to the response given by the children.

Since we believe it is important to provide students with immediate knowledge of the correctness of their responses, we considered this limitation very serious and made strong efforts to counteract it. Ideally, we would have liked to react immediately to each response given by a child, letting him know if his response is correct or, if incorrect, what he did wrong. This ideal teaching strategy can occur only with individual tutoring or computer-assisted instruction. With radio, the most closely we could approximate this ideal was to announce the correct answer just after the children responded, leaving the child to determine for himself whether his response was correct. A typical dialogue would be:

Radio teacher: Everyone tell me, how much is five times seven?
(Pause for response from classroom)
Radio teacher: Thirty-five. Five times seven is thirty-five.

Notice that after the pause for a response, the next words pronounced by the radio teacher are the exact response expected from the children; there are no intervening words or phrases, such as "Good" or "Correct" or "The right answer is . . ." After that, as further reinforcement, the radio teacher repeats both the exercise and the correct answer. The efficacy of this method relies heavily on the timing. If the pause is too short, the radio teacher will come in too soon and will be drowned out by the choral response in the classroom. If the pause is too long, the immediacy of the comparison is lost.

Another disadvantage of using a one-way medium is that the radio teacher is completely unresponsive to transient needs of the class. If a point is not clear, no one can question it. There can be none of the kind of interplay that occurs in good *discovery* teaching situations. Even a traditional lecturer can adjust better to the needs of the group; without a single question from the students, a sensitive lecturer can detect from their expressions when a point needs further explication. Because of the blindness of radio, a radio lesson must be prepared with much more care than a standard lecture.

So, in summary, of the four main characteristics of radio, we view the first—availability of the oral component—as advantageous. The second characteristic—no visual materials—is less of a disadvantage than many people think. The remaining two—being a mass medium and offering only one-way communication—are almost entirely disadvantageous, but not sufficiently so as to make impossible the design of effective instructional programs.

Costs

Costs played an important part in curriculum design, and indeed in all other project decisions, because the project lessons were not replacing some other component of the educational system that could then be eliminated to reduce the total cost. Rather, radio lessons were an add-on cost that the government would have to justify in order for the program to continue after external funding ceased.

Project costs are of two kinds: costs attributed to lesson development and those resulting from broadcasting and receiving lessons once they are developed (implementation costs). Since lesson-development costs are high, they seem a logical place to economize.

However, an analysis of the long-range economic aspects of the project (see Wells & Klees, 1978) reveals that the implementation costs are more significant. If the programs are to be used again and again for many years—and in the case of a mathematics curriculum there is no reason why they could not be—the production cost can be amortized over that time period. Most implementation costs, however, recur each year. Among them are the cost of transmission; the cost of radio receivers for the classrooms, their maintenance, and provision of power for them, either by battery or electricity; the costs of printing and distributing supplementary materials for the children, and guides and training materials for the teachers; and the costs of supervision of teachers. Although implementation costs vary with the geographical dispersion of classrooms, the number of children and classrooms involved, and availability of electric service, the costs of implementing the program are higher than the amortized cost of the production of materials.

The curriculum designer can influence many of the implementation costs. The cost of lesson transmission, for example, depends on the number and length of the programs. However, transmission costs are a small percentage of the total implementation costs, and reducing them does not effect much of a saving. On the other hand, the costs of four of the components *can* have a significant impact on implementation costs. These are: radios, supplementary materials for children, supplementary materials for teachers, and training and supervision of teachers.

The cost of the radio receivers themselves is high. Although inexpensive transistorized radios are available, these are not of sufficiently high quality for use in a noisy classroom of 20 to 50 children. Even though some distortion is allowable in that voice transmissions are less critical than other kinds of radio broadcasts, the power supplied to the speaker must be sufficient to allow all the children in the room to hear; thus, an investment of about $50 or more per receiver is mandatory. One way the total cost of receivers can be reduced is by arranging to have them shared by several groups of children. For example, a single receiver could run several speakers in different classrooms. We did not try this, however, since we had few schools in which single grades were divided into sections. Rather, we asked teachers in different grades to share radio receivers, which were then moved from one classroom to another between broadcasts for different grade levels.

This may not seem like a curriculum issue, but the solution we adopted did have a significant effect on lesson design. Although the distance between classrooms is not great, moving the radio may take two or three minutes, so we decided to fit each program into 27 minutes and broadcast three minutes of music between programs. Three minutes per day is 10% of the available radio time, a loss that might result in significantly less learning over a year's time. In this instance, at least, the cost issue dominated the concern for quality.

The implementation cost that is most affected by curriculum decisions is the cost of supplementary printed materials for the students. Indeed, implementation costs can most effectively be reduced by keeping the amount of supplementary material to a minimum. We compensated for the absence of materials by increasing the quality of the broadcast lessons. (Note the trade-offs here: Textbooks do not have to be absolutely clear because the teacher can provide explanations; oral messages would not have to be so precise if we could refer the children to illustrations.)

In first grade, we used individual worksheets to supplement many of the lessons; these worksheets were to be used only once, then discarded. One alternative to worksheets is reusable text materials. Our calculations showed that the cost of supplying a textbook to each child is prohibitively high. A second alternative is shareable materials—posters, for example. This solution has been used by a number of nonformal educational projects, apparently with considerable success. Our experience with posters was somewhat more equivocal. Although the illustrations seemed helpful to the children, the teachers did not always put up the right poster at the right time, in which case the effect was lost. After producing the first-grade lessons, we virtually abandoned printed supplementary materials and put our entire effort into producing effective instruction that did not depend upon project-supplied illustrative materials.

We think it quite likely that the lack of printed materials resulted in the children's learning less about geometry, fractions, and measurement than they might have. However, we think that learning numeration skills, including counting, reading, and writing numbers, was not adversely affected, nor was learning various arithmetic skills like addition and subtraction.

Teacher training and teacher supervision are also major contributors to the ongoing cost of an educational project. It is quite possible to spend more for these teacher costs than for all other implementation costs combined. Our solution to this problem was radical—to do without teacher supervision and to provide only minimal teacher training, no more than was absolutely necessary to inform the teachers of indispensable administrative and logistic matters. This information was conveyed in a single 3-hour training session held at the beginning of the school year. The effect of the absence of teacher training on the curriculum design is discussed below in the subsection on teachers.

One final source of implementation costs—the production of materials for teachers—was kept to a minimum throughout the project by producing only a relatively short teacher's guide (one page per lesson) that was distributed once a year, before the opening of school. Since the same radio lessons would be broadcast year after year, the teacher's guide is reusable, and its cost could be amortized over its years of use.

As we have already mentioned, cost considerations severely restricted the use of auxiliary media. We examine here each supplement, describing our experiences with it and how it was used to augment the broadcast part of the lessons.

Worksheets. The lessons for Grade 1 were the first lessons developed by the project. The decision to use worksheets grew out of our lack of confidence that we could teach mathematics to children without any printed supplementary material. However, from the outset we sought ways to reduce the number of worksheets needed. One successful tactic was to group topics so that every other lesson (after about the third month) was primarily oral. This way, the number of pieces of paper that had to be printed and distributed was greatly reduced.

After we had had considerable experience in producing lessons that did not need worksheets (especially the experience of producing second- and third-grade lessons, which used none), we revised the last third of first grade to eliminate the worksheets. Perhaps because of our accumulated experience, the revised series was an outstanding success; in a carefully controlled experiment it was shown that the lessons without worksheets yielded exactly the same achievement gains as the lessons with worksheets. This was a startling (and unanticipated) result and should alter the thinking of other projects using radio for instruction. At any rate, it was confirming evidence that our decision to dispense with worksheets in later grades was well taken.[1]

Posters. The next most expensive of our standard array of supplementary materials was the posters, which we used only in second grade. The posters were used solely for illustrations that we felt had to be rather precisely drawn, beyond what teachers could draw freehand on the chalkboard. These included illustrations for

---

[1] It must be said that the lessons that were affected by this experiment did not include some of the concepts that are most difficult to teach without good illustrations, namely, measurement of time and area, and the concepts of fractional parts. Also, rewriting lessons to teach the same content without worksheets resulted in lessons that were, on the average, 4.5 minutes longer.

fraction and area concepts, on which we had found the teachers to be rather weak. The posters were referred to during the radio lessons, so the correct assortment had to be displayed by the teacher before the broadcast. We used the posters in about a dozen lessons during the year, having designed them for multiple use. One difficulty we encountered was that the teachers frequently failed to put up the posters, or put up the wrong assortment, or put them in the wrong order. Performance levels in both fractions and area were not high in second grade, although it is not clear that children would have learned more if the posters were properly displayed. Because of the expense and the difficulties associated with using posters, we did not include them in later work.

Chalkboards and notebooks. Two other supplementary materials that we used after first grade were the chalkboard and the children's notebooks. We sometimes used these together, sometimes separately. Sometimes, the chalkboard was solely a source of illustrations that would be referred to during the radio broadcast; there might be, for example, numbers to read or objects to count. At other times, the teacher would put on the chalkboard arithmetic exercises that the children were to copy into their notebooks—but not solve—before the broadcast. The radio teacher would then help the children to solve the exercises during the broadcast lesson. Many times, the children wrote exercises directly into their notebooks, following dictation by the radio teacher. Even though dictation is a more time-consuming way of writing arithmetic exercises than copying, the time was not entirely wasted since the children got needed practice in associating written and spoken numbers, writing numerals, and in aligning the columns of exercises.

We used many drawings. At first, these were drawn on the chalkboard by the teachers, following the illustrations provided in the teacher's guide. The children could refer to these during the discussion conducted by the radio teacher. Later, the children copied simplified drawings into their notebooks, and still later they made the drawings for themselves following instructions given by the radio teacher. Drawings were kept simple: Marbles were drawn as small circles, boxes were represented by squares, other containers were triangular in shape, necklaces were represented as straight lines with small circles placed on them at intervals. We found that the children could draw these figures quite well and fairly quickly and seemed to enjoy doing so. Here again we found the added advantage that the children attended more closely to the explanation when they were making their own drawings than when they were merely looking at an already prepared illustration.

By the time we were working on the third-grade series, we learned that we were attracting a sizable out-of-school listening audience, which gave rise to the hope that eventually our programs might simultaneously serve two audiences—children in school and children and adults not attending school. Since an out-of-school listener can hardly benefit from those segments of the lesson that depend upon chalkboard illustrations, we chose to eliminate the use of the chalkboard as far as possible in fourth grade. All numbers, exercises, and illustrative drawings were produced by the children themselves under the guidance of the radio teachers. (By that time, the staff had become quite skilled at writing succinct yet clear instructions for such tasks.)

It is important to note in connection with both chalkboards and children's notebooks that there is no *add-on* cost of these auxiliary media, since the classrooms are already equipped with chalkboards and the children are ordinarily expected to purchase notebooks for use in mathematics classes.

Curriculum Content

In theory, we were constrained to teach the content set forth in the official syllabus produced by the Ministry of Education. In practice, it was difficult to abide by this constraint for several reasons. For one thing, the syllabus is a mixed bag of goals, objectives, pedagogical strategies, and justifications written for the average classroom teacher rather than for a curriculum designer. There are few clearly stated behavioral objectives, and it was sometimes difficult to tell when a description of a teaching strategy was an optional suggestion or a mandatory requirement. With each year's curriculum, our first task was to read between the lines to determine the intent of the syllabus and to transform it into a set of clearly stated behavioral objectives that would serve as the foundation for the year's course. Particularly unclear throughout was the area of technical vocabulary. When words like *commutative, additive,* and *identity* appeared in the syllabus, it was never clear whether these terms were to be taught to the children or whether they were simply being used to describe to the teacher the *concepts* that were to be taught. Since our own preference is to play down the use of technical vocabulary, we ordinarily opted for the latter interpretation.

Another difficulty that we encountered was that the fourth-grade syllabus had never been officially released. Although we were quite sure that many first-, second-, and third-grade teachers followed the official guide more or less closely, we were also quite sure that the same did not hold for fourth grade. We did manage to obtain a draft copy of the fourth-grade syllabus but found the recommendations to be somewhat unrealistic, demanding much more of the children than we thought they would be able to learn. According to an unofficial source, the reason behind the excessive demands was a Ministry proposal, several years back, to change the elementary course into a four-year course instead of the traditional six-year course. This came about, we understand, as a result of the UNESCO definition of a schooled person as one who had attended four years of school. Rather than eliminate content, the Ministry had attempted to fit six years of curriculum into four, with the greatest compacting occurring in fourth grade.

After reviewing this situation, and knowing that the traditional instruction was proceeding unaware of the content of the official syllabus, we used a completely different strategy for the construction of the fourth-grade lessons than we had used for first through third grades. We collected achievement-test data to find out how much fourth graders ordinarily learned and used this information to help us decide which of the recommended topics should be deleted from the curriculum. If we found, for instance, that a topic we considered questionable for fourth grade was poorly learned, we eliminated it from consideration. For many of the topics we tested, fewer than 20% of the children answered correctly; most of these topics were dispensed with in the radio curriculum. Even with this paring, the amount of material was still enough, or more than enough, for a single year.

Another problem with the official guidelines was in the sequencing of topics. The guides were generally divided into sections, each covering one topic, for instance, *sets, numeration, addition,* or *subtraction.* For each section, there was a recommended time allowance, for instance, *two weeks, three weeks, five weeks, three weeks.* From our observations of traditional classrooms we had learned that most teachers took these suggestions quite literally. They taught sets for two weeks, then switched to numeration, and never again reviewed any of the material taught in the first two weeks. In our view, elementary-school mathematics is essentially a skill subject that must be reviewed and practiced continuously in order to attain the high degree of skill necessary for further learning and for application in daily life. Also, there are a few quite difficult concepts (zeros, regrouping for subtraction, etc.) that must be taught and then retaught a number of times before all children internalize them. For these reasons, we quite drastically rearranged the sequence of instruction to allow for the necessary review and practice. The teaching of the most important topics, such as numeration and multiplication, was spread over most of the year so that the children could learn just a bit at a time and practice each new subskill sufficiently before the next was introduced.

Formative Evaluation

Because we were using a feedback model of formative evaluation rather than a revision model, there were special constraints on the curriculum design, primarily in the time schedule for the introduction of new topics. Our particular concern in this regard was that the students attain an acceptable level of mastery of prerequisites before a new topic was introduced. In individualized instruction this would be taken care of by having mastery tests at fixed points within the curriculum and not allowing the student to be exposed to new concepts until he had mastered the prerequisites. With mass media, mastery testing cannot be handled on an individual basis, but we could at least assure that *most* children had sufficient mastery if we could test the children before instruction in a new topic proceeded. Logistically, the steps involved are these:

1. Test the knowledge of prerequisites with a reasonably sized sample of the students.

2. Determine if the level of performance is sufficiently high.

3. If it is not, provide the necessary review before teaching the new topic.

All three of these steps take time, especially the last, which involves preparing new lesson plans, writing scripts, writing the corresponding teacher's guides, producing the tapes, and producing and distributing the guides. With a very tight production schedule, testing, analysis of data, and production of new lessons can be done in three to four weeks. To ensure, then, that we did not introduce an important topic before the children had mastered the prerequisites, we had to allow about a four-week hiatus between the teaching of the prerequisites and the teaching of the new concept. Of course, this did not mean that we stopped broadcasting. Rather, we filled the four weeks with instruction on other, unrelated, but equally important topics. For example, if introduction of a new division concept was being delayed, we used the time to teach topics in numeration, addition, multiplication, measurement, problem solving, etc.

Schools and Classrooms

School buildings in Nicaragua are generally poorly constructed, inadequate in size, and underequipped. With the help of a substantial construction loan from AID several years ago, a large number of rural schools were built. Although small and unattractive, these buildings are usually more adequate than the older, larger, urban schools.

The typical rural school is a concrete-block building with three or four classrooms, all with outside doors. There are no internal halls, and classrooms usually have large (unglazed) windows on opposite sides of the room, so there is adequate ventilation and light. Urban schools, in contrast, are usually barn-like buildings that have been subdivided into classrooms by paper-thin partitions. Many of the classrooms do not have windows and, consequently, have inadequate ventilation and light. The furniture is inappropriate and inadequate. Children frequently have desks and chairs that are either too large or too small. It is not uncommon to see four or five first graders squeezed onto a bench that was designed to seat two sixth graders. In classrooms with no desk tops or tables, children must use their laps or else sit on the floor so they can use their chairs as desks. In one classroom that we observed frequently, there were no desks or tables; the only chairs were small, unpainted, wooden rocking chairs that were packed so tightly into the room that no child could leave his seat without disturbing half a dozen of his neighbors.

Since the windows are always open and the walls provide inadequate insulation, the noise level in many schools is quite intolerable, especially in the urban schools where nearby industry and passing trucks may drown out all conversation for several minutes at a time.

It may seem that the above problems are not curriculum issues, and indeed there is little the curriculum designer can do to alleviate such problems. What he or she can do, however, is avoid exacerbating them. Knowing, for example, that the background noise level is sometimes excessive, the radio director uses only actors with clear, carrying voices. Important messages are not obscured by background music or sound effects. Even in the midst of a complete dramatization in which such effects seem almost mandatory, they are dispensed with during the time that a critical message is to be delivered. Also, in planning physical activities and games, we took care to use only activities that would be possible within the confines of the typical classroom. Children were not asked to form large circles, for instance, or to run across the room, since we knew that in most classrooms these would not be possible. When we asked the children to stand up to do a few simple calisthenics, we allowed sufficient time for those children who would have to wait for their neighbors to get up first.

In instructional segments, we took care not to ask the children to use concrete materials that would be inappropriate. Since many desk tops sloped, we never asked the children to count marbles or other small objects that would readily roll onto the floor. Although small pieces of paper might be good for counting activities in some situations, we did not use them again after observing 30 desk tops swept clean by a single gust of wind after the children had spent several minutes neatly arranging strips of paper into groups of 10 in preparation for a regrouping activity.

More important, since classroom supplies are almost nonexistent, we never asked the children to use materials that we had not previously warned them they would need. Pencils, also, were not supplied by the school system. Since most children preferred ballpoint pens to pencils, we could never ask them to erase errors.

We found we could count on only one item of equipment being present. We never observed, or heard of, a classroom in Nicaragua that did not have a chalkboard, although the condition of these was frequently deplorable. The chalkboards were usually quite small, however, so we took care not to ask for more chalkboard displays than could be easily accommodated, with the numbers and figures drawn large enough to be easily visible from all parts of the room. To accomplish this, we occasionally had to transfer planned segments to other lessons. Also, we ordinarily asked the teachers to start with only those displays that would be needed during the broadcast and then erase them afterwards to make room for displays to be used in postbroadcast activities.

Although many of these concessions to classroom limitations seem trivial, lessons that do not take them into account may be nearly unusable in many classrooms, or at least so awkward to use that teachers would soon come to prefer teaching mathematics without radio.

By far the most important of the classroom limitations was the ubiquity of multigrade classrooms; over half the rural teachers in Nicaragua teach more than one grade. If we wrote radio programs that could not function without the minute-by-minute support of the classroom teacher, it would mean that her attention during the broadcast would be entirely diverted from the other children whose rights to her time were just as valid as those of the children to whom we were broadcasting. A much better arrangement would be for the radio broadcasts to act as surrogate teachers so that the classroom teacher could be free to attend to children in other grades; the result would be better instruction for all children in the classroom, not just for those hearing the radio lesson. To accomplish this is no small task since it means that the radio lessons must be completely self-contained and understandable to the children without intervention. The means by which this was accomplished have been discussed in other places.

Teachers

Although we never conducted extensive studies of the knowledge and classroom behavior of the Nicaraguan teachers, we did come to know their strengths and weaknesses quite well from several small formal questionnaire and interview studies and even more from the many hours of classroom observations that we made as part of the formative evaluation of the curriculum material.

In general, their classroom behavior and teaching styles differ little from those of teachers observed in many different countries, including the United States. In classroom management, they seemed quite as effective as teachers anywhere; discipline is generally good without being oppressive, and the teachers are respected and liked by the children they teach. There is a marked tendency to play the role of lecturer, and there is little individualization of instruction and little attempt to foster discovery learning. However, ability grouping is quite common, especially in first grade where most classes are divided into three ability groups. (We have been told that this grouping procedure is a direct result of an intensive teacher-training program undertaken a number of years ago as part of a Point-IV program.) This grouping is fairly inflexible throughout the school year, the lowest group being identified by the teacher early on as the children who will not pass the grade and will be expected to repeat it the following year. This group usually receives a disproportionately small amount of the teacher's time (thus leading to a self-fulfilling prophecy; see Tilson, 1978). Although grouping in second grade is less common, it is not unheard of, and where we instituted a small experiment that required the teachers to use ability grouping there was no resistance to the idea. For all grades we frequently suggested small group activities for the postbroadcast portion of the lesson and found that our suggestions were followed by almost all teachers.

In administrative matters, Nicaraguan teachers are somewhat more relaxed than U.S. teachers; in particular, they are less anxious about time schedules, a reflection of the entire society's attitude toward time. This relaxed attitude imposed at least one constraint on the curriculum design. Since we could not rely on teachers to turn the radio on at exactly the right time, we could not start the day's lesson with a sequence of instruction in which it was critical that the children hear every instruction from the beginning. For instance, suppose a lesson opened with dictation of an exercise. Any child who did not hear the first part of the segment—and copy the dictated exercise into his notebook—would not be able to understand the remainder of the discussion. Such a segment is best placed in the middle or near the end of the lesson. We started all lessons with segments that could be understood even if the first part was not heard; these were usually oral drill, songs, and the like.

A more serious limitation arose from the teachers' lack of knowledge of mathematics. Most Nicaraguan teachers attend school for only 11 years and do not have more than the equivalent of a high school diploma. Although they are generally quite adept at conventional arithmetic, and have some concept of "new math" ideas such as sets, they frequently have a very shaky understanding of topics like geometry, area, and fractions.

This lack of knowledge, which could have been overcome by massive in-service training, was one of the biggest determining factors in the decisions about which topics to put into the radio broadcasts and which to put into postbroadcast activities. If we found that the teachers themselves did not have an adequate understanding of a concept, we frequently allocated radio time to that concept even though the topic was not well suited to that mode of presentation. There is no doubt that much of this instruction was of lower quality than we would have liked, but the only alternative would have been to increase the costs enormously, either in teacher training or in additional supplementary materials.

In several instances, we would have liked to make substantive changes in the traditional content of the mathematics course— changes that we believed would have improved the children's achievement significantly—but did not do so because of anticipated teacher resistance. One case in point is the division algorithm. This algorithm, which is used widely in the Latin American countries, is demonstrably less useful than the division algorithm commonly taught in the United States. We saw no reason why the children could not learn one version as readily as the other, but we saw that without extensive teacher preparation we could not institute such a change. Unless the teachers themselves fully understood the variant algorithm, they could not help individual children. And unless they saw the need for change, they would be quite likely to try to teach the children the traditional Latin American method for division. Since the two methods are quite similar in form and since division is difficult to learn in any case, we feared that children exposed to an alternate method would become hopelessly confused and that the result would be worse than teaching the less useful Latin method.

Another, similar case involved the use of "leading zeros" in subtraction exercises like:

$$\begin{array}{r} 67 \\ -\ 62. \\ \hline \end{array}$$

In the United States, children are taught to write the answer as 5, whereas in Nicaragua they are allowed to write 05. Technically, of course, 05 is numerically equivalent to 5 and might be considered the correct answer. But, as one of our baseline studies showed, children who wrote 05 did not realize this equivalence; when asked to read such a number they frequently said "fifty," indicating a basic confusion about the properties of the decimal system of numeration. We would have liked to have taught the children not to write these leading zeros, but again we felt that without adequate teacher training we were doomed to failure. As a compromise, we spent a considerable part of a number of lessons teaching the children that 05 and 5 are equivalent, so that they would at least be able to interpret their subtraction results meaningfully.

Although teachers expressed some initial doubts about the usefulness of radio as a teaching aid, there was little serious resistance to the innovation, and most teachers became quite enthusiastic about the radio lessons after using them. This was particularly important to us since, as we saw it, the key ingredient in the eventual success of the project would be whether the broadcasts reached their intended audience, the children. The teachers, as our only means of access to this audience, had to perceive the value of the radio lessons both as a means of improving the educational opportunities of their young charges and also *as a teaching assistant who could reduce their own workload.* This is not a matter of laziness or disinterest in the job but a matter of necessity in a country where a teacher may be forced to deal with 40 to 100 children in up to three different grades, with no financial support for materials or supplies either from the school system or the community. Teachers in such situations *cannot* take more tasks upon themselves no matter how much the additional effort might contribute to their efficacy as educators.

The Broadcast Audience

At the outset, we thought the target audiences were teachers and children in school. Later, we broadened our view to include out-of-school listeners as well (see chap. 8). In this section we first consider the children's languague limitations, their incoming skills in mathematics and in general knowledge, and their school attendance patterns. Then we discuss the out-of-school audience of adults and children who are not in school and consider how their needs affect program design.

Language. Because children have limited language capabilities, we used a very restricted vocabulary in instructions or other speeches that we expected *every* child to understand. Since there was no previous research into the recall and recognition vocabulary of the Nicaraguan children, and we did not have time or resources to make an extensive study before commencing production, we simply learned from experience, adjusting the language of the lessons as it became apparent from observations or from conversations with the children that they either did not understand some critical words or that they had a greater vocabulary than we had previously suspected. The only formal study of children's vocabulary that we undertook while in Nicaragua was a study of the words children used to name the pictures that we wanted to use for illustrations on the first-grade worksheets.

In controlling vocabulary (and syntax) we made a strong distinction between *critical* and *noncritical* uses of language. Any question that we expected the children to answer or any instruction that we expected them to follow was what we call a critical use of language. In these parts of the programs, we expected every child in every classroom to understand the intent of the question or instruction. This did not mean that we expected every child to respond correctly—only that every child understand what the task required. These critical uses of language are to be distinguished from noncritical uses that occur in asides made by the radio personalities or in the entertainment sections.

Even within an instructional message there may be both critical and noncritical words and phrases. If a worksheet has pictures of five animals that are the same kind and we want the child to circle three of these, we might use an instruction like the following:

> Radio teacher: Look at your worksheet. See all the giraffes drawn on the worksheet. There are five giraffes altogether. Take your pencil and circle three of the giraffes.

Since there is only one kind of animal shown on the worksheet, it matters little whether the children know exactly what kind of animal a giraffe is; they will understand what is being referred to, and what task they are to do. In this case, the word "giraffe" is not used in a critical way. On the other hand, if there were more than one kind of animal shown, the distinction would become critical, and so would the word.

We frequently needed to use words that were not already in the children's vocabulary. In that case, we took care to develop an understanding of that word before it was used critically by teaching the word in a natural way. We would start by introducing the word in a noncritical way in a message that we were quite sure all children would be listening to, for example, one of the feedback messages delivered by a radio teacher just after the children had responded to some exercise. After a number of occurrences of the word, preferably spread out over several lessons, we would start to use it in a critical sense but accompany it by paraphrases that would make clear to the children what we meant.

After the word was well established in the children's recognition vocabulary, we would teach the word for recall by asking the children to respond to questions for which that word was the correct answer. At first we did not ask them for free recall; instead, we embedded the word in an oral multiple-choice exercise, so that they were selecting the correct word and saying it aloud. The following oral multiple-choice exercise might be used to teach the children to recall the words "one-fourth" (after they had already learned "one-half" and "one-third"):

> John cut the cake into four parts, all exactly the same size. When there are four parts, all the same size, do we call each part one third or one fourth?

At a later time we would ask the children to recall the word, using exercises like this:

> John cut the cake into four parts, all the same size. What is each part called?

Our students, like children everywhere, had poorly developed listening skills when they first entered school. They could not listen to long messages and generally preferred activities that did not rely much on verbal abilities. For entertainment they much preferred physical games and calisthenics to the more verbal stories, jokes, and riddles. In concession to their tastes, we relied heavily on nonverbal activities whenever possible. Even to mark the transition from one activity to another we used musical cues rather than verbal announcements of the change in topic.

However, since we had to verbalize the mathematical ideas we were teaching, we could not rely forever on physical activity and music and so had to try to increase the students' listening skills. We have already discussed some of the ways we increased their vocabulary. The other major effort we made in language development was aimed at increasing their ability to attend to, as opposed to comprehend, spoken language.

One facet of this involved gradual speeding up of speech. At the beginning of each year, the radio teachers spoke at a slower than normal speed. This rate was gradually increased, so that by the end of the year they were speaking at a normal, or faster than normal, rate.

We also encouraged the children to listen closely, not by constantly reminding them to pay attention but by showing them that it was in their best interest to pay close attention. The two main devices we used for this were to eliminate nonessential messages and to keep repetition of messages to a minimum. By reducing the number of nonessential messages we produced scripts with a high information content. Almost every message said something meaningful or interesting. A child who did not listen missed something of importance to *him*. If his mind wandered for a moment he suddenly found that all his classmates were busily starting an activity that he was missing, or that they were laughing at a joke he had not heard. This kind of peer-group learning is much more effective than any number of warnings to listen closely or to pay attention.

We also rarely repeated a message verbatim; to do so would cause the children to learn that they need not listen the first time since we will always say the same thing again. This is not to say that there was no redundancy in the radio programs. There was—for several reasons. One is that spoken language, unlike written, is transient. Important points must be repeated and paraphrased, perhaps several times. Also, in teaching mathematics, the same concepts have to be reviewed many times and the skills have to be practiced, and practiced again. What is best, however, is to provide this redundancy in an ever-changing context. We had children practice the same skills in many, many exercises. But we did not use exact repetition to get across a point.

Incoming skills. A clear idea of the incoming skills of the students is essential in designing efficient and effective instruction. If initial instruction is aimed too low, valuable instructional time is lost. If aimed too high, the children will not understand the instruction and will not be able to keep up the pace. In addition to language, we were particularly concerned with general knowledge and previously learned mathematical skills. In the first year of production we had not yet had time to test fully the incoming skills of the children in any of these areas and had to rely on the recommendations of supposedly informed sources, mostly from the Ministry of Education, including the official curriculum guide published and distributed by the Ministry. In doing so, we were partly misguided. The official curriculum guide recommended to first-grade teachers that they spend about three weeks at the beginning of the year developing *basic skills* such as comparisons of size, length, and height. They were then to introduce the concept of sets as a preliminary to concepts in numeration, in particular counting and comparisons of numerosity of sets. After our first few weeks of classroom observation, and especially after studying the results of the first-grade pretests, we found that the children already had well-developed skills in simple comparisons of height, length, numerosity, etc., and that they also had considerable counting skill. Because we had not anticipated that the children would have these skills, most of instruction we designed for the first few weeks of the first-grade program was unneeded and therefore inefficient, a fault that we corrected in the revision made in the next calendar year.

The problem of incoming skills arises afresh at every grade level. One of our particular problems was that at the beginning of every grade except first we had two distinct audiences of school children, those who had had previous instruction by radio and those who had not. Since the radio instruction was considerably more effective than traditional teaching, the children who had had radio lessons in the previous grade were quite far ahead of the others. Our problem was, should we aim the radio programs at the group who had taken radio lessons the year before or should we try to prepare a curriculum package that could be used by all children regardless of their previous schooling? This problem is not unique to radio-based instruction but applies equally to the design of any instructional innovation that spans more than one grade level. Although mobility is typically low in Nicaragua, there are many children who repeat grades or who do not attend school every year. We felt it necessary to accommodate all children and thus designed lessons at each grade level for a mixed population of children, some of whom had and some of whom had not had previous experience with radio lessons. Since we had to review many topics that our former students had already learned, the programs were less efficient than they would have been if we had been able to count on a completely stable population.

Because Nicaraguan children, like children everywhere, do not have a very long attention span, we were not sure how long lessons should last. We experimented during the first year with programs that varied in length from 15 to 30 minutes. During the same period, we were also experimenting with lesson formats, language, and different kinds of entertainment, as well as with the pace and content of programs. After much classroom observation, we concluded that the total length of the program was not as critical as the content and style. If we changed topics and pace often enough and put in enough devices to capture and hold attention, even the first graders seemed to pay attention well for a half hour. (This may not be true of all first graders; the average age of the Nicaraguan first grader is about eight and a half.) Some of the techniques we applied to hold the children's attention were asking for frequent audience participation in both the mathematical and the nonmathematical segments of the lesson, changing voices of radio teachers every few seconds, using both male and female voices, using child actors, inserting frequent entertainment breaks with highly varied content, and keeping the pace very fast.

Attendance patterns. It was not unusual for children to be absent for a day or two because of illness, because they were needed at home, because the road to school was flooded, or because of local saint's days. Even when the children were physically in school, they occasionally missed radio lessons because of special activities. Also, tardiness was quite common. Whatever grade was receiving the first broadcast of the morning was quite likely to miss the first part of many broadcasts because either students were late or the teacher was late.

Because we anticipated that absence rates might be high, we did not prepare the lessons as if every student had received every previous lesson. Thus, we put in a large amount of review, especially when introducing difficult topics. In reteaching a topic, we frequently presented the idea from a slightly different point of view so as to maintain the interest of those children who had not missed any lessons and to help those slow learners who had not grasped the concept when it was first presented, as well as to teach it for the first time to children who had been absent.

Out-of-school audience. As we mentioned earlier, over the years we developed a relatively large outside listening audience. We received letters from some of those listeners and heard anecdotal reports of many others. (At a later time, an informal audience survey was undertaken to determine the extent of the out-of-school audience; see chap. 8). Many of these listeners were adults who had never attended school or who had not been able to complete their elementary schooling; at least one of our listeners was a grandmother, but most of the audience were young adults, and there were some children who for one reason or another were not able to attend school.

After we became aware of this audience and also aware of the growing international interest in the use of radio for nonformal teaching of formal school subjects, we tried to adapt our programs to the needs of the out-of-school audience in ways that would not reduce the effectiveness of the instruction for the primary (in-school) audience.

The situation of the out-of-school audience differs in two substantial ways from that of the in-school audience. First, there is no teacher (and no teacher's guide), so any parts of the broadcast that are substantially supported by the teacher are lost to them. For instance, if a teaching segment refers to exercises or numbers that have been written on the chalkboard by the teacher before the broadcast, the references are lost on the out-of-school audience. Second, for the same reasons, the postbroadcast activities are not available to the out-of-school audience.

To accommodate this audience, we made a number of changes in language and teaching strategy. For example, beginning in third grade, we addressed the listeners as *muchachos* (young people) rather than as *niños* (children), and we reduced the number of casual references to the classroom situation or to the classroom teacher. In fourth grade we took an even more drastic step, which involved the very basis of the curriculum design. Knowing that postbroadcast activities would not be available to some of the audience, we used the radio broadcasts to cover all of the most important topics, including particularly those that would be most useful in the daily lives of Nicaraguan citizens. Thus, the radio lessons could, by themselves, serve as a self-contained course for an out-of-school audience.

Logistics

In Nicaragua, as in most developing countries, physical transportation of materials to remote areas is quite difficult. Outside the capital city and away from the two or three main highways there are few paved roads. Although most schools are accessible by car, the roads are poorly maintained and frequently closed during the rainy season. Four-wheel-drive vehicles are often a necessity. A few schools can be reached only by boat, and in the mountainous areas some schools can be reached only on foot or horseback. There are no reliable delivery services to rural areas, although the postal service reaches most of the towns reasonably well. Telephone service is poor in the towns and nonexistent in rural areas.

These deficiencies caused innumerable problems for the project, leading to many inefficiencies in production. With sufficient money and determination, we were able to cope with the problems that arose during the experimental phase of the program; our concern was about what would happen in following years when the program was implemented on a much broader scale. It seemed clear that the Ministry of Education could continue the program only if the logistic problems were minimized.

In planning for the future, we saw three major difficulties that might be alleviated by careful planning of the curriculum packages. These were problems

(a) of delivering materials to the schools,

(b) of gathering teachers together for training, and

(c) of providing ongoing supervision of teachers.

To all three of these, our approach was essentially the same: We tried to reduce or eliminate the need that would give rise to the difficulty. Over the years, we reduced the need for supplementary materials to almost nothing. Although the first-grade program requires a worksheet for every individual child, the materials required for second grade are less bulky than the teacher's guide itself. And both the third- and fourth-grade programs can be used with no supplementary materials for the children; only a teacher's guide is needed, and since this guide can be used year after year, the problem of regular deliveries of materials to the school is solved. Of course, our primary reason for reducing supplementary materials was cost rather than logistics; this is one of the cases in which two constraints worked in the same direction.

Partly because of the difficulty of gathering teachers together for training sessions and partly because of the costs of a massive teacher-training program, we also worked toward the elimination of teacher training. After some experimentation, we settled on a single three-hour training session per year, but even in the experimental phase, not all teachers were able (or willing) to attend these meetings. To ensure that the necessary information was available to all, we included in the teacher's guides and in the brief handouts (broadcast schedules, for example) that were distributed along with the guides the same information as was presented in the training sessions. One cannot, of course, simply eliminate teacher training without also compensating in other ways for the lack of training. We did this by making the curriculum package so easy to use that special training was unnecessary. This is a nontrivial solution and one that consumed a large part of our resources.

Most innovative projects also plan for follow-up supervision of teachers to help them implement the training program. We judged it highly unlikely that after our departure the Ministry of Education would provide any supervision beyond what was already in place in the educational system. Therefore, we decided at an early stage not to involve ourselves in an extensive follow-up program. As in the case of teacher training, the solution was to provide a curriculum package that made no unusual demands upon the teachers. None of the prebroadcast or postbroadcast activities required skills or knowledge that we did not expect all teachers to have. And for the broadcast portion of the lesson, all that the teachers were required to do was to turn on the radio. This is, of course, crucial. Although the children themselves might be viewed as a captive audience, their teachers are not.

We employed several stratagems to enlist the cooperation of the teachers. We tried to make the value of the radio lessons apparent to everyone, even a casual listener. Beyond that, we tried to hold our teacher audience by providing them a service that made their tasks easier, not harder. In particular, the radio curriculum required less preparation time than traditional instruction. This was accomplished in two ways. First, we did not require the teachers to prepare many special materials for the postbroadcast activities. And we ensured that the materials we did require would be easy to find in any community in Nicaragua. Second, by providing immediate feedback to the children during the broadcast, we eliminated much of the need for grading papers. Also, we did not ask the teachers to obtain supplies beyond simple objects the children could collect themselves. The value of some of the instruction would have been enhanced if the children could have used simple equipment and supplies like construction paper, scissors, rulers, and measuring cups. However, these are not furnished by the Ministry of Education, and had we required them, teachers would have had to purchase them from personal funds.

In our concern for gaining and keeping the support of the teachers, we were also careful not to present controversial subjects or language in the radio programs and we used only mathematical terms or concepts that we knew were familiar to the teachers.

4. WHAT COULD WE HAVE DONE DIFFERENTLY?

Taking into account all the factors that shaped the curriculum design, did we make the best possible decisions and produce an optimal solution to the pressing problem of inadequate mathematics instruction in the public schools of a developing nation? Or were there things that we could have done better?

Certainly there were things we could have done differently. Whether or not they would have been improvements is left to future projects to determine.

We could have used a different lesson format, with fewer long segments, perhaps. We could have used more—or less—entertainment. We could have put some mathematical content into entertainment segments instead of insisting on such a strict division between work and play. Our language could have been less—or more—colloquial. These changes would probably not affect the children's mathematical achievement much, but might have been desirable for other reasons.

Another alternative, for which a strong argument could be made, would be to prepare second-, third-, and fourth-grade programs only for those children who had previously received radio lessons. With an essentially nontransient population such as that in Nicaragua, the cumulative effect of several years of radio lessons would have been much higher without doing serious harm to transferring students (most of whom could catch up with extra help from the teacher). Certainly, a program that is used nationwide or even over a fairly wide region would not be disadvantageous even to transferring students who would, for the most part, have had radio lessons in their previous school.

Had we been willing to violate the constraints a bit, especially the cost constraints, there are several changes that would undoubtedly have improved the curriculum. We could have taught measurement of all kinds more effectively and more extensively if we had allowed the luxury of even a few worksheets a month. Measurement of length, weight, area, time, and money are important and useful mathematical topics that we slighted by leaving them in the hands of teachers who did not have adequate tools or knowledge.

There are a number of ways (several of which we have already mentioned) in which the curriculum could have been improved if better training had been provided to the teachers. This, again, is mostly a cost consideration, since teacher training is expensive. But there are also logistic considerations. How would we get to the teachers, or the teachers to us? Especially after the experimental phase, how would Ministry personnel, who have few cars and limited funds, manage to conduct teacher training in remote rural areas? One solution, often suggested, is teacher training by radio. The cost of this is not insignificant, but it does dispense nicely with the logistic problems and does not require training of teacher-training personnel. This is an idea that we considered quite seriously from the beginning but rejected for reasons unrelated to costs. In the early years, we did not think we knew enough about what makes an effective radio/ teacher team to be able to train teachers to be more effective than they already were. Now, after several years' experience, we are beginning to get a good idea of how a teacher should behave and what he or she should know to use radio as an effective teaching aid, and we have an idea of what part of this could be transmitted to him by radio and how to go about it. It is still not clear, however, how much improvement in the children's performance could be effected by such an addition to the curriculum package, nor whether the teacher training would be cost-effective in terms of achievement gains.

REFERENCES

Tilson, T. *Teaching first-grade mathematics by radio: Observations in six Nicaraguan classrooms* (Tech. Rep. 300). Stanford, Calif.: Institute for Mathematical Studies in the Social Sciences, Stanford University, 1978.

Wells, S., & Klees, S. Education decisions and cost analysis for the Radio Mathematics Project in Nicaragua. In P. Suppes, B. Searle, & J. Friend (Eds.), *The Radio Mathematics Project: Nicaragua, 1976–1977.* Stanford, Calif.: Stanford University, Institute for Mathematical Studies in the Social Sciences, 1978.

Formative evaluation of a product is carried on while the product is being developed in order to improve the product before it is released for wide consumption.

In this chapter, we describe the feedback *system of formative evaluation and contrast it with the* revision *system. The feedback system, which is an integral part of curriculum production, is a systematic approach to producing curriculum materials; when applied correctly, it ensures a high-quality product that is well suited to the needs of those for whom the materials are intended. The heart of this system is the timely collection and interpretation of meaningful data from a group of subjects who adequately represent the target audience.*

Before selecting the experimental subjects for evaluation, it is necessary to specify the target audience. In our case, it was not the few thousand children using the project materials during the experimental phase of the project but, rather, future generations of schoolchildren in all parts of Nicaragua. To choose a sample that would fairly represent this target audience, we had to speculate about what schools would be like in the future.

In our imagination, the future classroom would be in a remote, rural area of Nicaragua. It would be no better equipped than the poorest of the classrooms we had seen in our experimental area. The room would be overcrowded with children, and the furniture would be insufficient and inappropriate. The lighting and ventilation would be poor; there would be no electricity, and no water. The only equipment would be a worn chalkboard no larger than three feet by four feet. For supplies, the teacher would have chalk, and each child would have a small notebook that he or she had purchased. The teacher would be young, with only a few years' teaching experience, and with less than 10 years of formal schooling. There would be no textbooks, so the teacher would be forced to make lesson plans with no more guidance than a syllabus from the Ministry of Education. And the worst problem would be that the children would not all be in the same grade, so the work of making lesson plans and carrying them out would be doubled or even tripled.

One day, due to the generosity of some remote governmental office, the teacher would receive an inexpensive radio, a teacher's guide to the radio mathematics lessons, and a schedule of the daily broadcasts. The radio would originally come equipped with batteries, but replacements would be left to the teacher to provide. There might or might not be a local teacher-training session to acquaint the teachers with the nature and purpose of the radio broadcast, and if there were such a meeting, it might be so far away or at such an inconvenient time that our teacher could not attend.

A more experienced teacher, self-confident of her ability to teach mathematics, might simply disregard the whole project and take the radio home for personal use, but our young teacher, unsure of her ability to teach a subject she herself does not understand and fears, would try one of the lessons. Because she would find nothing threatening or incomprehensible in the broadcast lessons, because the guide would provide her with ready-made lesson plans, and because the children would seem to enjoy listening, she would continue to use the programs almost daily. She would have to carry the radio to and from home every day, since there would be no locked room or cabinet in the school, and she might occasionally forget it and a lesson would be missed. Luckily, the next lessons would review the missed material, so the children would not suffer a serious setback. Because the teacher would have no watch, she would not always turn the radio on at the right time. Sometimes when this would happen, the children could not immediately pick up the thread of the lesson, but within a couple of minutes, a different topic would be introduced and the children would busily engage in the suggested activities.

On occasion, a few of the children might have difficulty with some of the exercises presented by the radio. Most of the time, the teacher could provide the help they need because the method required for the solution of these exercises is the same as the one she learned in elementary school. But if the children have some difficulty that she could not remedy, there is no one she could turn to for assistance. There would have been no continuing teacher training, the district supervisor's office would be too far away, and there would be no local curriculum consultant. All she would do is ask the children to continue listening to the daily radio lessons in hopes that the misconceptions would be dispelled at a later time.

This, then, was our view of the future and our task was to select classrooms that would have as many of these characteristics as possible. The sample we chose would be observed and tested regularly to ensure that the curriculum materials we were preparing would be adequate for the children of the future.

Having once selected the sample, we had to see to it that our intervention in the classrooms would not change the character of the sample classrooms so much that they would no longer be representative of the future target audience. The difficulties of remaining a nondisturbing presence in the classrooms chosen for the collection of formative evaluation data were never completely overcome—as will be seen from the discussion found in this chapter—although seemingly satisfactory compensatory measures were taken.

Chapter 3

A HISTORICAL VIEW
OF THE USE OF FORMATIVE EVALUATION
BY THE RADIO MATHEMATICS PROJECT

JAMESINE FRIEND

FROM ITS INCEPTION, the Radio Mathematics Project has made use of formative evaluation techniques. However, during the course of the project the particular methods employed and the uses to which the results were put have changed markedly. This chapter describes the evolution of the formative evaluation system we now call the "feedback" model, which we believe is particularly well suited to the development of a long-term intensive instructional program.

While we were, from the outset, committed to using formative information in the development of lessons, we had no preconceived notions about methods and strategies. We began with the traditional method used in mass media projects—design and produce a sample lesson, try it out, then revise it—and we expected our experiences to help us assess the suitability of the method for our needs. In short, we expected to apply (informal) formative methods to the formative evaluation system itself.

We had many data sources available to us—classroom observations, student written work, student interviews, teacher interviews, tests. We had to choose among data sources and to decide how we would use the data we collected to modify lessons. The first section of the chapter describes our early methods for collecting formative data and applying the results to lesson design; it then discusses how our experience with these methods led to the development of the new model. The second section describes the new feedback model and how it was implemented, discussing the relative merits of several outcome measures and how the results obtained were used in the lesson production process.

1. EARLY FORMATIVE EVALUATION EFFORTS

The California Trials

The first efforts at lesson-testing were conducted in California with the standard tryout-and-revise paradigm. Our view at the time was that, despite cultural differences, children in different countries are sufficiently similar that a preliminary trial would provide useful information. (Our assumption was subsequently supported; the major lessons learned in California applied to Nicaragua as well.) In the spring of 1974, we prepared a set of five lesson tapes and presented them in two kindergarten and two first-grade classrooms in a school close to Stanford University. First grade was selected because we planned to start curriculum development at the first-grade level. We included the kindergarten classes to test our procedures with children in their first year of school, since first grade is usually the first year of school for Nicaraguan children. (As it turned out, our reasoning was quite wrong. In fact, as many as 40% of Nicaraguan first graders have had previous school experience both because of the high repetition rate and because many children audit at least part of a year before formally enrolling in school. Also, the average age of Nicaraguan first-grade students is about eight, as compared with six in the United States, so in many ways they are more mature and hence more comparable to American second graders.)

In the California field trials we were not concerned with the mathematical content of the lessons. Because of our previous experience with the development of mathematics curriculums, we already knew a great deal about appropriate levels of content for American children; further information about appropriateness for a Nicaraguan audience would have to be collected in Nicaragua. Rather, we wanted to test lesson formats and instructional techniques that we thought would be effective in radio lessons.

From deficiencies in the California lessons we learned many useful things that enabled us to go into preliminary trials in Nicaragua with more confidence. Simply by observing the children we learned a great deal. We learned that children were able to follow lessons that changed topics frequently. This type of lesson organization, which we call a segmented structure, is based loosely on the design of the successful Sesame Street television series and on lessons designed for delivery by computers. We wanted to use it because it allows practice in many different topics each day and because changing topics is a good device for maintaining student interest.

We also learned a great deal about using student worksheets. We designed worksheets that looked much like those used in ordinary

U.S. classrooms and found that many of our California subjects simply could not find the right place on the worksheet to write their answers—a combination of problems with the worksheet itself and with the oral instructions. It became clear to us that, because the radio teacher cannot *show* the children where to write their answers, both the worksheets and the instructions for their use must be designed with special care. However, our trials convinced us that worksheets could be used in conjunction with recorded instructions without constant individual supervision, even with children as young as six years old.

We learned to be careful not to ask children to look at two different things at the same time, the kind of mistake that is obvious in retrospect but difficult to avoid in practice. For example, we asked the teachers to hold up a large replica of the worksheet and show the children where the radio lesson was asking them to direct their attention. This was quite ineffective since the children could not attend simultaneously to their own worksheet, the teacher, and the oral instruction. If their attention had been directed sequentially from one to the other, it probably would have worked; we later found techniques of instruction that allowed children to use both notebooks and chalkboards simultaneously. We never pursued the idea of using the teacher as a demonstrator because it was evident that more carefully prepared oral instructions could free her for more useful activities, for example, attending to the needs of individual children.

Thus, the California trial provided us with clear evidence that our concept of how to design radio instruction (based on a segmented structure) was viable, and we came away with constructive ideas about how to improve the format. We also learned that observing lessons in the classroom is essential for producing materials that children could use.

The First Nicaragua Trials

We repeated the experience in basically the same way in Nicaragua a few months later. After observing regular first-grade classes and studying the official curriculum guide, we selected a few mathematical topics that would be appropriate for our audience, wrote two lessons, and tried them out in two classrooms. We incorporated all that we had learned from the California trials; by then we had also hired an experienced radio producer-director so that the results were much more professional. Each lesson had a theme story that incorporated several segments, each covering a different mathematical topic.

Once again, we found that the instructions were sometimes ambiguous and there were several points at which the story did not hold the children's attention. We therefore revised the lessons and wrote four more. Then all six lessons were tested in a larger number of classrooms. We observed the children quite closely and also analyzed in considerable detail the answers children wrote on the worksheets.

By this time the lessons had a fairly high "face value," that is, the children listened attentively, followed the directions well, and appeared to be enjoying themselves and to be learning. By using the format that had undergone several successive revisions and by applying the same general principles of instruction writing, we were able to produce lessons that seemed reasonably effective. We did not believe these lessons to be perfect, but we did not think we would learn much more from short-term experimentation. What we needed was a much longer sequence of lessons so that we could start to measure learning gains over longer periods of time. Although the children appeared to be learning, there was no guarantee that they were learning at a satisfactory rate or that they would retain what they had learned if such instruction became part of their regular daily program.

The process we described above, in which lessons are prepared, tried out with a small audience, and then revised, is well known and widely used in education. The underlying assumption of the model is that a specific product (a lesson, for example) can be improved by testing it with representative members of the target population and making the changes suggested by the data obtained from the field test. Note, however, that we were getting more than suggestions for improving the lessons we had already designed. Our field testing was yielding information that enabled us to write *new* lessons that were better than what we could have written had we not done the field testing at all. In fact, the new lessons, even without field testing and revision, were as successful (by the same criteria we had used previously) as previous lessons that had been tested and revised. In other words, the "specific product" that we had been field testing was not the individual lessons but the instructional techniques that were used in those lessons. Since the same, or similar, techniques of lesson formatting, phrasing of instruction, design of worksheets, etc., were used in new lessons, it was *not necessary* to field test and revise each individual lesson. We now needed to refine the methods we had developed and to assess the effectiveness of a longer sequence of lessons.

2. THE FEEDBACK MODEL

The model we chose was an adaptation of the feedback system used in industry to control continuous processes. In this model the output is continuously monitored and any deviation from the desired outcomes causes an automatic compensatory adjustment of the input parameters. Although we could not fully automate this procedure, we did devise a production schedule that incorporated continuous monitoring of the output (learning gains, children's attitudes, etc.) so that input parameters (teaching techniques) could be adjusted to optimize the outcomes.

This model we will call the "feedback" model in distinction to the "revision" model used in our first field trials in California and Nicaragua. One of the most noticeable differences between these two models is that in the feedback model there is *no revision of lessons*. Each lesson is prepared and field tested, but the information gained is not used to revise the existing lesson; instead, it is used to revise teaching and presentation strategies so that future lessons will be better than they would have been otherwise. (In practice, of course, we correct obvious errors, as we mention later.)

By the beginning of the next school year (February 1975) we were ready to go into full production using a feedback process. During that year we produced a full year's curriculum that proved to be of high quality even though no lessons were revised during the year.

The feedback system as we used it entails these steps:

1. Closely monitor outcomes.
2. Analyze the data to determine how instructional techniques can be improved.
3. Use the revised techniques in the design of future lessons.

Monitoring Outcomes

Step 1 seemed the largest problem in our first attempts to systematize the feedback model. What outcomes are to be monitored? And by what means?

We were primarily concerned with student outcomes: how well students followed taped instructions, their level of interest, their misconceptions, their rate of learning, and their retention of concepts and skills. We had already found that watching children during lessons was a most fruitful means of gaining information, so from the outset we included daily observations as one of our primary sources of information.

Classroom observations. Our methods for observing and recording the results evolved considerably over the course of the project. In the first field trials our observations had been quite unstructured. In 1975, when we started regular lesson production, we attempted to systematize the observation process, designing special observation forms that helped the observer focus on specific aspects of the lessons and organize his comments.

We also made an effort to train ourselves as observers. Since no one on the staff had had much experience in classroom observations, this was a bootstrap operation and our first efforts were relatively unsuccessful. Most of us, especially those with strong training in research, felt that observations were unreliable. In debriefing sessions we picked apart one another's observations and argued endlessly about how to measure such things as "interest" and "attention" in more reliable ways. However, we soon came to realize that our attempt to transform observational data into "hard" data went too far; although our observation forms provided quantitative results, the effort to quantify was so engrossing that we often missed more important classroom events. We eventually backed down from this fruitless attempt to quantify what is essentially unquantifiable and later even encouraged observers to do more "interpreting" instead of simply reporting in a factual way the events they observed.

Despite these problems, the classroom observations were the most useful information we collected, especially in the early stages. It was from the observations that we learned what kinds of entertainment the children preferred, how long the lessons could be and still hold the attention of the children, how long instructional segments should be, what kinds of instructions were ambiguous, how fast the pace should be, and how long we should pause for children to complete different tasks like writing numerals, solving addition exercises, or making simple drawings; and so on.

Much of this information came from long-term observations and could not have been obtained from watching a single lesson. The entertainment value of a joke, for example, depends somewhat on its novelty. We learned how often jokes could be repeated before the novelty wore off. On the other hand, sing-along songs gain in value with repetition. As the children learn the words, they participate more fully and enjoy themselves more. Our observations gave us information about how many times and at what intervals to repeat such songs. Instructional messages, too, can be evaluated only in the context of fairly long sequences of lessons. An instruction like "Circle the third animal" might be too terse for most first graders, but it is quite understandable to children who have been trained gradually with more wordy instructions like "Look at the animals—Find the *third* animal. Draw a circle around that animal."

Analysis of student worksheets. Although classroom observations are immensely valuable, there are some kinds of information that they yield poorly or not at all. Suppose that the children are solving a worksheet exercise like

$$\frac{\begin{array}{r}3\\+\ 4\end{array}}{}$$

under the tutelage of one of the radio characters. This exercise goes by rather fast in real time and it would be difficult for an observer to determine exactly how many students in a classroom of 40 or 50 youngsters had answered it correctly. Even harder to observe are the kinds of incorrect responses made. Incorrect responses are frequently very revealing of the nature of the misconceptions children have, and it is important to collect such information. However, during a typical radio lesson the proportion of correct responses is very high, on the order of 90%, so only three or four students are making errors; it is unlikely that the observer will spot more than a few of the errors.

For such additional information that cannot be obtained by observing, we turned to the children's worksheets. During 1975 we collected all completed student worksheets. The responses were coded, keypunched, and analyzed by computer. We obtained information on each exercise, summaries for each instructional segment, and lesson summaries. The data included the proportion of correct responses, and for each exercise a list of the incorrect responses and their frequencies. Examination of the proportions correct, within each lesson and over time, gave us the rate at which the children were learning the various topics covered by the lessons. Whenever the learning rates were below expectations, we looked more closely at the incorrect responses, which frequently helped us pinpoint the conceptual difficulties that were causing the low learning rate.

When we were unable to determine the sources of difficulty, we alerted the observers to watch closely as the topic was being taught to see what insights they could gain into the issue. In this way we discovered that the feedback process could provide information not just for lesson development but also for the feedback process itself. (At a later time, after we had established testing as a regular part of the monitoring operation, we found that analysis of test data indicated where closer observations would be helpful.)

The worksheet data were extremely useful and had the advantage of being much "harder" data than we could obtain from observations. However, as the year went on we became somewhat dissatisfied with their usefulness as indicators of performance levels. The proportions correct on the worksheet exercises were extremely high and, for several reasons, did not adequately represent how well students were learning the mathematical content of lessons. For pedagogical reasons the radio personalities were giving the children the correct answers to almost every exercise shortly after the exercise was given. Some children changed their answers as soon as the correct answer was announced, and a few children (probably not knowing how to proceed) would wait until they were told the correct answer before filling in their worksheets. Teachers were encouraged to help the slower children work exercises during the lesson and frequently children worked together, helping each other.

Another cause for concern was the lack of information about retention of skills. In a general way we knew that the children were retaining the skills, because in mathematics new skills and concepts usually build on those already learned; children could not continue successfully if they had not retained the prerequisite concepts. In cases where there was trouble with a new concept, however, we did not know whether the difficulty was caused by a deficiency in prerequisite skills or our instruction in the new concept was ineffective. Also, there were some topics that were taught and then not used immediately. Did the children's skills deteriorate rapidly in those areas or were they well retained?

Embedded tests. About halfway through the first-grade school year, our dissatisfaction with worksheets as a data source, and some teachers' interest in evaluative information, led us to consider ways of testing the children. Regular tests of about five or six minutes' duration were embedded into the curriculum and occurred once a month. From the children's point of view, the tests looked much like any other instructional segment. The instructions were given in the usual way and used the regular student worksheet. The tests differed from instructional segments in that the radio characters did not announce the correct answers and a mixture of different types of exercises were given. (The usual instructional segments had one or at most two kinds of exercises.)

The embedded tests were more useful than the worksheets in providing a picture of learning gains, and the results helped us spot several difficulties that we had not previously noticed. Furthermore, we found that, despite our doubts, the children were retaining concepts and skills quite well.

To satisfy the teachers' needs we included in the teacher's guide an answer key to the embedded tests along with suggestions on how to use the tests for diagnosis. We instructed the teachers to grade the tests if they wished and to use them for their own purposes before sending them to us. (They regularly sent us all worksheets.) If they did not want to use the test results themselves, they could simply send us the ungraded papers. Apparently very few teachers used these tests in the way we had anticipated, because only about 10% of the returned papers had marks that indicated that the teacher had graded them.

Weekly classroom tests. Although we were getting more reliable data, we were not convinced that embedded tests were the final answer to our problems. For one thing, we did not want t·) produce a completed instructional package that contained tests that were not going to be useful to teachers. If we were the only ones who were going to use test data, then the tests should be used only during the developmental phase and not included as an integral part of the released version of the curriculum. Furthermore, it was difficult to design tests to serve two purposes (diagnosis of individual difficulties—which would be useful to teachers—and feedback for curriculum development), so at the end of the first year we gave up the idea of embedded tests in favor of an auxiliary testing program whose only purpose was to provide feedback for curriculum development. We also decided we needed performance information more frequently than once a month. From 1976 on, we used weekly tests administered by project staff in selected classrooms.

An even more significant change in the testing program was our adoption of matrix-sampling design techniques. Once we were freed from the constraints of preparing tests that could serve for individual diagnosis, we could concentrate on our principal testing goal—to measure how well the children *as a group* were progressing. We wanted to measure learning for a large number of curriculum objectives (on the order of 200 every year), and for each objective we needed to test the children at enough different points during the year to be able to measure gains. Also, to get a reliable estimate of the performance level for an objective, it was necessary to use more than one test item. To accomplish all of this we would need weekly tests of 100 to 150 items, obviously too many items for an individual child to handle. Since we wanted to measure *group gains,* not individual gains, it was not necessary either to test the same children every week or to give the entire test to any one child. So we divided each test into several 15- to 20-item subtests and tested different children each week, rotating the testing within a fixed group of classrooms so that the same children were tested again after three to four weeks, a technique known as matrix sampling. (We used the same group of classes for logistic reasons, not because we needed data from the same subset of children.)

Over the next three years we varied the parameters (test length, number of subtests, frequency of testing the same children) of the test design only slightly. We highly recommend this method for the formative evaluation of any curriculum material, whether delivered by radio or by other instructional media, because it can provide information about many different topics.

Using Feedback Data

From 1976, when we developed the second-grade curriculum, until Stanford involvement in the project ended in December 1978, we used the weekly tests and daily observations as the two major means of monitoring the outcomes of the instructional method. The feedback system involves more than simple data collection, however. The second step in the feedback process is the analysis of these data with a view toward finding where improvements and refinements of instructional techniques are needed. In most cases, the goal is not simply to move closer to a unique solution to the "Which way is best?" question but to continuously alter the parameters of the instructional techniques to keep up with the changing needs of the children. For instance, there is no single best time allowance for solving exercises like 28 + 5. When children are first introduced to these exercises (in the second grade) they will slowly and laboriously count from 28 on, probably using their fingers or tally marks on paper to help them keep track of the counting process. After some practice they will consistently use a smooth, very fast counting algorithm, and after considerable practice they will answer so quickly that it appears they have the answer memorized. What we try to do is watch the children closely as we gradually decrease the time allowed. For this particular example the best (in fact, only) information on which to base a decision for change comes from classroom observation.

Other changes are based on test results. For example, one difficulty children have is not attending to the operation sign in exercises like

$$\begin{array}{r} 43 \\ +\ 21 \end{array} \qquad\qquad \begin{array}{r} 43 \\ -\ 21. \end{array}$$

A very common error is the use of addition when subtraction is indicated, and this shows clearly in the answers written on test papers. To help the children, there are innumerable reminders in the radio programs to look at the sign. When the children's responses to test items show that they are beginning to heed these cautions, the frequency of such reminders is reduced in the radio scripts.

Thus, we see that what may at one time be a "perfect" instructional technique may at another time be unnecessary and inefficient. The feedback process, unlike the revision process, is a dynamic system of formative evaluation. Its aim is not so much to correct gross errors as to refine and alter instructional techniques in step with the changing demands of the audience.

This is not to say that feedback does not also help in detecting errors. Ambiguities in instructions, for example, may be detected by either observations or testing, and an effort must be made to correct such errors in future programming. Errors of great magnitude, however, cannot always be compensated for by the feedback process and usually require lesson revision. If the introduction to some important basic concept is badly presented, the children may form misconceptions that can never be entirely dispelled. For this reason the feedback system is not useful in the early stages of development. It was only after we were sure we could produce lessons with good face value and no serious errors that we could effectively use a feedback process to refine the techniques.

Small errors can be tolerated without damaging the overall effectiveness of the feedback process. Any project that is producing material at the rate of one radio program per day is bound to produce trivial errors from time to time. We produced one tape, for example, in which the answer to 4 + 3 was 8. Annoying and embarrassing as these small errors are, they do not cause more than momentary confusion among the children and do not slow the overall rate of progress. We do not like to see the errors repeated year after year, though, so we did revise the master tapes as soon as such errors were reported. Thus, we continued to use the revision system in a small way even when relying most heavily on the feedback system for lesson improvement.

In all of the examples mentioned so far, the kind of change needed can be immediately inferred from a knowledge of what happened in the lesson and in the classroom. However, the solution is not always so obvious. On several occasions we have produced instructions that clearly did not work; the children could not understand the examples, looked puzzled, could not follow our instructions, and performed poorly on the tests. We had put our best effort into designing the instruction and could see no other method that looked equally promising. We had no option but to try one of the alternatives that we had previously rejected. In some cases the second method worked; in others it did not, and we had to try again. In one case (comparison of mixed numbers), after numerous attempts we abandoned the objective as too difficult to teach by radio at that grade level; we do not know whether that judgment was correct or we were simply too limited in imagination to provide the right kind of instruction.

Error analysis. Frequently, when a solution was not immediately forthcoming, we found it quite helpful to analyze the test data in more detail. Our usual procedure was to administer the weekly tests during three days of each week (we did not have enough personnel to test children in all classrooms on the same day) and to complete the first analysis of the data in the next two days so that the curriculum designers and scriptwriters could see the results within one week. The first analysis consisted simply of grading the papers, finding the proportion of students who correctly answered each item, and comparing those proportions to previous proportions correct for the same objective. If the learning gains were not satisfactory and the causes were not self-evident, we did an error analysis, which, on most occasions, provided us with great insights into the misconceptions held by children and gave us an immediate clue to the ways we could improve the instruction. Sometimes we were uncertain of our interpretations of the children's thinking processes, so we asked observers to watch the children closely as they solved similar problems during the radio lessons. We later found that structured interviews with the children were a better source of information. The children happily explained to us in detail the (incorrect) procedures they were using to solve arithmetic exercises. This method provided invaluable information, and in the future we would use it more extensively.

   Trade-offs. By far the most difficult problem in the entire feedback process is that of deciding trade-offs. If 100% of the children are giving correct answers to some kind of test item, we know we can reduce or eliminate future practice on that kind of exercise. But suppose only 90% of the children answer correctly. Do we then continue the practice until we reach 100%? The easy answer is to say we should have some predefined "mastery level," like 90% or 95%, established for each objective and provide sufficient instruction to reach that level. (What this mastery level is, or how one should go about determining it, is never specified by those who suggest this decision-making process.) The problem is that there are usually many objectives in which the children are not yet performing at mastery level. How do we make the decisions about trade-offs? Even worse, do we have sufficient information to know where the possible trade-offs are?

   These questions have implications both for methods of collecting information and for the methods of analyzing and acting on that information. The following example illustrates the first situation. Suppose two objectives, A and B, are equally important and that the children are performing at the 30% level on A and at the 50% level on B. If we had information only about performance on B, we would probably decide to give more practice on B. But providing more practice on B means spending less time on other topics, among them objective A. If the objectives are equally important, we have made the wrong decision simply because we lacked information on A. This example makes clear that all important objectives must be tested frequently enough to allow us to extrapolate learning curves with confidence (a good reason for using a matrix-sampling design for the tests).

Even with sufficient information in hand about all important objectives, the decisions about allocations of instructional time are still extremely thorny. We gave considerable thought to the allocation problem and did develop a theoretical distribution algorithm that seemed quite satisfactory. Unfortunately, the algorithm was so complex and used such a large data base that the computation required a high-speed computer. We had no such computer on location and the logistic difficulties of using the computing facilities at our home base at Stanford were so great that we were never able to implement the scheme. Allocation decisions were made by hand, using a subjective weighting of the objectives, taking into account both the prerequisite relations between objectives and the probabilities of transfer of learning between related objectives.

The prerequisite relationships are important in cases where the trade-off under consideration is between two objectives A and B, with A prerequisite to B. If the performance is quite low in both topics, it may be wise to give preference to A since the low performance in B may be due to prerequisite deficiencies. On several occasions we have seen the performance in B increase satisfactorily when only A was allotted more practice.

In subjects with many related skills, instruction in one skill or concept often improves performance in another. This phenomenon, called transfer, plays an important role in curriculum design. The probabilities for transfer between related objectives are quite subtle to evaluate and an awareness of the various linkages comes only through intensive study of vast amounts of performance data collected over time. Once one knows that transfer is occurring, it is usually trivial to explain why, but transfer does not always occur in places that one might expect. The trick to detecting transfer is to look for learning gains in the absence of instruction and to try to relate the rate of gain to the amount of instruction being given in other topics. If we had taught the topics in isolated units, this task would have been easier, but we were frequently mixing the teaching of half a dozen fairly new topics with practice on another half dozen previously introduced subjects. More basic research in this important pedagogical area is certainly needed.

Another consideration in allocating time to various topics is the expected gain from more practice. If there are two objectives A and B, both equally important and both with low performance levels, we might consider weighing the "payoffs" we would get from more time spent on A as compared with time spent on B. If the learning curve for A is quite steep compared to B (meaning that learning occurs faster with A), the total learning will increase more by practicing A than by practicing B. Here, again, there is so little basic research that almost all decisions are ad hoc.

The preceding paragraphs have illustrated many ways that feedback, in particular test information, is used in making curriculum decisions. Collecting such information in a timely fashion requires a comprehensive procedure for choosing test items. In general, we measured performance on a selected set of instructional objectives at many points in the school year, both before and after the topic was taught. Roughly, the testing schedule was developed as follows.

1. List all instructional objectives for the year, together with the proposed schedule for teaching.

2. Select those objectives to be tested. We were not able to test all objectives adequately, so there had to be trade-offs between the number of objectives that could be tested and the number of times each objective could be tested.

3. Schedule the objectives for testing, using the following rules:
   a. Test each objective just before and just after it is taught to get good measures of the effectiveness of the initial instruction.
   b. Test each objective again at regular intervals through the end of the school year.
   c. Test each objective at regular intervals before the pretest that immediately precedes instruction, from the beginning of the school year. This provides measures of entry-level skills and indications of where transfer has occurred from other related objectives introduced earlier in the course.

Pitfalls of testing. Sometimes the results of a detailed analysis of the test results revealed that the difficulty was not with the instruction but with the test items themselves. Ideally, we should have started each year with an item pool of valid, reliable test items for each objective. To establish such desirable characteristics of test items is itself a time-consuming process that requires much field testing, analysis of data, revision, and re-trial, which our schedule did not permit. What we did, instead, was to use a bootstrapping operation in which we tested the tests as we were testing the children. When we found items with questionable validity, we simply ignored the results, revised the items, and tried again.

A more likely source of error than bad test items was deficiencies in the specifications of objectives. We frequently found that our item pools were not homogeneous: Some items were significantly more difficult than others in the same item pool, indicating that the skills required were not identical for all items in the pool. This was valuable information not just for test design but for curriculum design as well, for it helped us improve our task analyses of the various algorithms we were teaching the children. For example, we found that the item pool for simple borrowing

$$
\begin{array}{ccccc}
57 & 83 & 61 & 50 & 80 \\
-\,29 & -\,47 & -\,14 & -\,35 & -\,37 \\
\end{array}
$$

is not homogeneous; the last two items are markedly more difficult than the first three. That discovery was our first clue that children had the most difficulty deciding to borrow when the upper digit is zero, and this led to a significant improvement both in the lessons and in the tests.

Selecting classrooms. So far we have hardly mentioned the children we were observing and testing. Since the end result of the feedback process is to tailor the instructional package to the children tested and observed, it is important to select classrooms that are representative of the audience for whom the instruction is intended. We ordinarily selected about 12 classrooms. Since this is a very small sample, we could not select at random, because of the possibility of a random bias. Instead, we selected classrooms that (to the best of our knowledge) represented the diversity found nationwide. Some classrooms were in fairly large schools in medium-sized towns; others were in small rural schools. Some had experienced, older teachers, while others had young or inexperienced teachers. Some classrooms included several grades in the same room; others had only one grade. Some had as many as 50 or 60 students; others as few as 10 or 12. After the first year, some of the children had had radio lessons in previous years; others had not. Some of the teachers favored small groups and gave individualized instruction, while others worked only with the class as a whole. In one case we had two teachers who combined their classes so they could team teach. We tried also to select some "good" teachers and some "not so good," following the advice of the local school inspectors.

We were somewhat constrained logistically to choose schools that were reasonably accessible, since we wanted to visit them frequently. None of the schools we observed regularly was more than a half-hour's driving distance from the office, and all could be reached by four-wheel-drive vehicles. Some of the schools were inaccessible for a few days during the rainy season, but we did not ordinarily have many problems getting to the schools until the political disturbances started in 1978.

A problem that is perhaps even more serious than selecting typical classrooms is ensuring that they remain typical. Our interference in those classrooms could easily become so great that after a few weeks the character of the classrooms could be completely changed. If, for example, we provided more teacher training than would be given when the programs are used nationwide, the data we collected might indicate that the children were learning quite rapidly; the effect, however, might be due to the additional teacher training and not to the parts of the curriculum package that would later be available to all classrooms. While teacher training was fairly easy to control, ongoing teacher supervision was an even greater problem. Because of the costs, we could not anticipate that teachers all over the country would be supervised any more closely after the advent of radio than they were during the development of the curriculum. So we did not want to provide additional supervision or continuing training to the teachers in the feedback group. However, we visited these schools regularly, and our mere presence could be interpreted as supervision at some level even when we disclaimed the intent. Also, the teachers viewed all of us as experts in teaching mathematics and we were frequently asked for advice on how to conduct certain activities, how to improve certain teaching strategies, and what to do about specific children. All observers were cautioned (frequently) not to offer suggestions or criticisms, but few can successfully sidestep direct and persistent questioning. It also happened on several occasions that teachers forgot to bring the teacher's guide. Observers ordinarily carried a guide (to help them organize their comments) and could hardly refuse a direct request to lend it to the teacher.

Our presence also influenced the children (though perhaps to a lesser extent, since children more readily accommodate themselves to being observed). What child will not put forth just a little more effort knowing that some adult is peering over his shoulder? The greatest direct effect on the children was from the testing. Even though we did not test the same children every week, the testing schedule resulted in testing each child 8 to 10 times during the school year. As the children learn test-taking skills, their performance improves; some increases in test scores probably could not be attributed to learning gains.

Although many of these factors had little or no noticeable effect by themselves, the total cumulative effect was nevertheless significant. For two years we made a posteriori comparison of the gains of the formative evaluation group with a comparable randomly selected group that had not been observed and tested, and the results clearly showed that the formative evaluation group performed better on the posttest.

There is no way to completely avoid this so-called Heisenberg effect of the observer on the observed, but it can be compensated for to some extent in the interpretation of the data. We always assumed that if the children in our formative group experienced some difficulty with a concept, then our intended audience would have that same difficulty to an even greater degree. If any of our teachers misinterpreted the teacher's guide, we assumed that the difficulty would be multiplied at a later time and should be corrected for. Although the classes we observed used the radio lessons quite regularly, we did not assume this would be true when we were not in the classrooms, so we built in more redundancy and more review than our observed children seemed to need. These were all truly subjective judgments and we may on occasion have overcompensated.

Changes Resulting from Feedback

As mentioned before, the feedback process has three major components: collection of data, interpretation of data, and adjustment of instructional techniques and other design parameters. We have looked at the first two of these components. Let us turn now to the kinds of changes that resulted from the feedback process. Recall that the feedback process is not used for correcting gross errors, since only future lessons are involved. The kinds of changes that result from feedback are changes in the design parameters on which future materials are based, and in most cases there is no fixed "best way," since the needs of the children are constantly changing. The design parameters that were changed as a result of feedback include the following.

Length of radio programs

Length of instructional segments

Mix of instructional and entertainment segments

Style of transitions between segments

Interval between programs for different grades

Syntactic complexity of instructional messages

Vocabulary

Length of instructional messages

Frequency and duration of dialogues between radio personalities

Frequency of student responses

Kinds of responses

Time allowed for different kinds of responses

Kinds of background sounds used during such pauses

Signals used to indicate the ends of pauses

Speed of speech

Mix of different kinds of voices

Mix of adult and juvenile voices

Use of juvenile voices for cuing student responses
Kinds of jokes
Way of teaching lyrics of songs
Amount of instruction on different topics
Spacing of review exercises
Rate for phasing out supportive instructional messages
Rate and style of knowledge-of-results messages
Format of the worksheets
Selection of other supplementary manipulable materials
Frequency and style of use of the classroom chalkboard
Layout of the teacher's guide
Number of activities in the postbroadcast period
Kinds of postbroadcast activities
Style of instructions written in the guides

The above—and other—changes that resulted from the feedback process can be categorized by the points at which they enter into the production line. So let us diverge momentarily to discuss the production process.

We started each year with a detailed plan for the content of the year's lessons. This plan included exact specifications of the behavioral objectives and the prerequisite relationships between these objectives. It also included a time schedule indicating when topics should first be introduced. The schedule was tentative, since we planned to change it as indicated by the information we collected from observations and testing.

Incorporating Changes into Lesson Production

During the year, the detailed outlines for each day's lesson were written as late as possible, so that if changes in the original plan were needed, the effect of the changes could be felt in the classroom as soon as possible. We usually planned about four weeks for the whole production process but on many occasions cut this lead time to three weeks or less. During that time, besides writing the lesson outlines, we wrote and edited the scripts, wrote the teacher's guide, produced the tapes, duplicated and distributed the guides, broadcast the program, observed and tested the children, and analyzed the feedback data.

The time schedule for production is illustrated in Figure 1. To get a sense of this process, we will follow through the production steps for lessons that are to be broadcast in Week 24, which are outlined in black. At the top of the figure, note that during Week 21 we are preparing the lesson outlines for Week 24. Moving down, during Week 22 we are writing scripts and teacher's guides. During

PRODUCTION ACTIVITY	WEEK				
	21	22	23	24	25
Lesson outline	For week 24	25	26	27	28
Script writing	23	For week 24	25	26	27
Teacher's guide	23	For week 24	25	26	27
Radio production	22	23	For week 24	25	26
Duplication of guides	22	23	For week 24	25	26
Distribution of guides	22	23	For week 24	25	26
Broadcast and observe	21	22	23	For week 24	25
Test and analyze data	20	21	22	23	For week 24

FIGURE 1. A portion of the lesson-production time schedule.

Week 23 the radio programs are produced and the guides are dupli-cated and distributed. During Week 24 the programs are broadcast and observed. Finally, in Week 25 the children are tested and the data are analyzed.

Now let us look back up the steps listed under Week 25. At the bottom of the column, note that we are analyzing the effects of the lessons given during Week 24. If there are changes we want to make in different design parameters, the length of time it will take for those changes to be felt in the classroom will depend on the production step in which the change is to be implemented, as we shall see. Looking at the top of the column for Week 25, we see that the outlines for Week 28 are being written. If there are changes we want to make in lesson outlines (delay the introduction of some topic, review a topic that was presented earlier in the year, etc.), the earliest implementa-tion date will be Week 28. In other words, what we learned as a result of our experience with lessons in Week 24 will not affect the mathe-matical content until four weeks later. Moving down, we see that during Week 25 the scripts for Week 27 are being written. If the

PHILLIPS MEMORIAL
LIBRARY
PROVIDENCE, COLLEGE

changes we want to make affect the script-writing process itself but not the lesson outlines, the effect will be felt in the classrooms three weeks after the decision to change is made. These changes might affect the length of pauses for student responses, the mix of male and female voices, the kind of entertainment, etc. The manuscript for the teacher's guide is prepared concurrently with the scripts, so any changes in the guides will also be implemented within three weeks. These might be the number of postbroadcast activities, the language used in describing activities, or the kinds of illustrations used.

Moving farther down the Week–25 column, we see that radio programs for Week 26 are now being produced and that guides are being duplicated and distributed. And changes that affect studio production (but not scripts) can be made now and will reach the classroom in only two weeks. Such changes might be the volume of background music, the speed of speech, or intonation patterns for certain kinds of instruction. Finally, during Week 25 we are observing children as they take Week–25 lessons. If the data just analyzed indicate a need for closer observation of some aspect of the children's behavior, we can start those observations within one week of the time the need was felt.

Thus, we see that the feedback loop is not a single loop that feeds from the classrooms into the beginning of the production process but is a series of loops of differing sizes feeding into the production cycle at several points.

3. SUMMARY

Beginning with a relatively conventional notion of formative evaluation—which we have called the revision model—our work has led us to the development of a new model uniquely suited to the production of a large set of closely linked and interdependent lessons, as is typical of a sustained instructional program. The model can appropriately be used after a basic lesson format and key instructional strategies have been designed. One of its chief advantages is that it allows the production of a year-long instructional program within one year, saving time and resulting in a much lower total cost than that associated with the revision model, since re-recording lessons is not necessary. The feedback method of formative evaluation is certainly a significant factor in the success of the Radio Mathematics Project instructional program.

The most important question posed to the Radio Mathematics Project was, How much mathematics can children learn from radio? Can they learn at all? And, if so, do they learn more than they would have without radio? It is these questions that this chapter addresses.

The answers are to be found only by conducting a carefully planned formal evaluation of the differences in learning gains between children who take radio lessons and similar children who do not. This kind of evaluation, frequently characterized as "summative," is distinguished from formative evaluation, as described in the last chapter, by both its methodology and its goals. Summative evaluation is judgmental; it is intended to evaluate the curriculum package as a whole and in comparison with other alternatives (in this case, traditional instruction in the absence of radio).

For this task, unlike the formative work described in chapter 3, there must be a large sample of subjects taken at random to ensure the reliability of the statistical analyses and the inferences drawn from them. The measuring instruments (tests) must also be more carefully constructed to avoid measurement error. And the results are not to be tempered by intuitive judgments.

In order to make inferences to a larger (future) population, the treatment of the experimental group must be carefully matched to the treatment that will be received by the eventual target audience. Although, as pointed out in chapter 3, some difference in treatment can be tolerated (and interpretively compensated for) in formative evaluation, this must be minimized in a formal summative evaluation. For this reason, there can be no overlap between the formative experimental group and the summative experimental group. Thus, the children discussed in this chapter are not in the same classrooms as those studied in chapter 3, although the schools were located in the same region of the country.

One similarity between the formative evaluation discussed in chapter 3 and the summative evaluation here is the design of the tests used as measuring instruments: In both cases, a matrix sampling design, discussed in detail in this chapter, was used. They differ, however, in that the items used for summative evaluation were more carefully prepared, every test was field tested to ensure validity, and oral test instructions were tape recorded to minimize the variability of test administration.

Chapter 4

MEASUREMENT OF THE EFFECT
OF RADIO MATHEMATICS LESSONS
ON STUDENT ACHIEVEMENT

BARBARA SEARLE AND KLAUS GALDA

A MAJOR GOAL of the Radio Mathematics Project was to improve the quality of mathematics instruction in Nicaraguan primary schools. Thus, assessment of student achievement was a central and continuing task of the project. This chapter brings together the results of studies conducted over a three-year period. Earlier reports on some of this work are in Searle, Suppes, and Friend (1976) and in Suppes, Searle, and Friend (1978). We describe here the tests we used for measuring student performance, the methods of analyzing those results, the evaluation design and its implementation, and, finally, the results of the evaluation.

1. THE ACHIEVEMENT TESTS

Project evaluations of achievement were based on the results of a pretest and a posttest for each grade level. There were no tests available that had been written for all of Nicaragua, nor had any of the published tests been standardized for the Nicaraguan population. Achievement testing in Nicaragua was customarily at the classroom or school level. Because the project had no Nicaraguan tests to draw on, all pretests and posttests were adapted or designed specifically for project use.

Seven different tests were used to evaluate the instructional programs for Grades 1 through 4. (The posttest for Grade 3 and the

The authors thank Professor Robert Hornik and Edward George for critical readings of earlier drafts of this chapter.

105

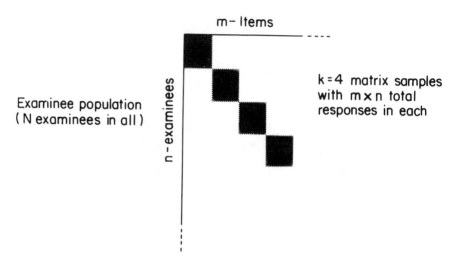

FIGURE 1. A testing design using matrix samples of equal size.

pretest for Grade 4 were identical.) All but the pretest for Grade 1 were based on a matrix-sampling design. In the next section we describe this test design and the rationale for its use. We leave until a later section the description of the pretest for Grade 1, which was an adaptation of a commercially available mathematics "readiness" test.

Matrix-sampling Design

Matrix sampling is a technique of test construction in which both test items and students are randomly sampled ("matrix" refers to this two-dimensional aspect; Lord, 1962; Lord & Novick, 1968). Figure 1 illustrates this notion. Consider a population of students of size N and a population of test items of size M. In Figure 1, the set of students is partitioned into groups of n students and the set of items into groups of m items. Thus, all subsets of students are equal in size, as are the subsets of items. In the example, each mutually exclusive subset of students takes a test consisting of one subset of items.[1] Subtests are constructed by randomly assigning items (without replacement) to test forms; the test forms are then distributed at random to students. Statistical analysis of data obtained from matrix-sampling designs assumes random assignment along both dimensions (Shoemaker, 1973).

---

[1] This is the simplest type of design; the sizes of the student subsets need not be equal; similarly, the sizes of the item subsets need not be equal. Subsets of items or students can intersect (Shoemaker, 1970).

Matrix sampling has the advantage of producing data on large numbers of items. However, this test design has the disadvantage that total scores for students taking different test forms are not directly comparable and statistical procedures must be applied to produce a total test score for each individual. In the early planning of the project, our concern lay primarily with comparing instructional programs, not with assessing the performance of individual children. Thus, the advantage of obtaining a rich data base outweighed the uncertainties associated with calculating individual test scores (see chap. 3), and we decided to base the construction of our tests on matrix sampling.

The particular design used for most project tests, illustrated in Figure 2, is more complicated than the basic one shown in Figure 1. Many items that test elementary arithmetic concepts and skills must be

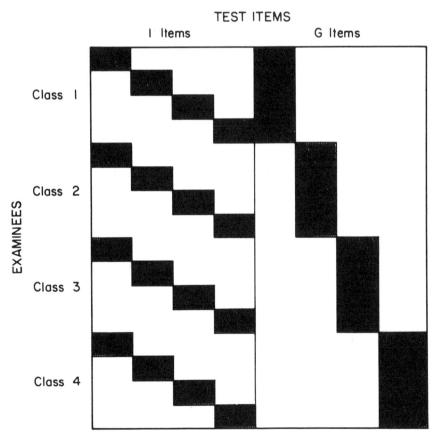

FIGURE 2. Matrix-sampling design of first-grade achievement test.

given orally; in each such case all children in a classroom must be tested on the same item. For other items, a more general instruction can be read aloud. As a result, two types of items were used that differ in the character of their oral component.

1. *Group item* (**G** item). A specific test item is read aloud, and all children in the classroom must answer this item.
   Example: "Write the sum of 23 and 42."

2. *Individual item* (**I** item). Only a general instruction is read aloud, so that the printed component of the item can be different on different test papers.
   Example: "Circle the largest number."

Group items cannot be assigned to students at random, since the same item is used for all students in a classroom. Hence, for these items, the assumption of random assignment of items to students is violated. Items were designed to be *individual* items wherever possible to avoid the classroom bias introduced by *group* items. (Bias arises from the common experience of the students in a classroom, meaning that the responses of individual students within the class are not independent.)

The posttest for Grade 1 exemplifies the structure of a project-designed test. The total number of items on that test is 84—44 **G** items and 40 **I** items. The **G** items are divided into four groups of 11 items. Each group is called a **G** *form* (labeled for convenience A, B, C, D). The **I** items are similarly divided into four groups or forms (labeled I, II, III, IV) of 10 items. In preparing the subtests that will be distributed to students, each **G** form is paired with each **I** form. Thus, there are 16 different subtests, labeled AI, AII, AIII, AIV, BI, . . . , DIII, DIV, each composed of 11 **G** items and 10 **I** items. Four subtests are randomly distributed to students in a classroom, namely, all the subtests with the same **G** form. Suppose that Form C is assigned to a classroom. Then each student in the classroom would receive CI, CII, CIII, or CIV; no other subtests would be distributed in that classroom.

To summarize, the posttest for Grade 1 consists of 84 items divided into four **G** forms and four **I** forms. Each student takes a subtest consisting of one **G** form and one **I** form. The **I** forms are distributed at random to students within classrooms; the **G** forms are distributed at random to classrooms. Although the basic structure described here was used for most project tests, the numbers of items and numbers of forms differed. Table 1 presents the characteristics of the tests used at different grade levels. Test sizes range from 84 to 144 items; the number of items taken by each child ranges from 21 to 36.

TABLE 1

Characteristics of Project Pretests and Posttests

Grade	Type	Total no. of items	No. taken by each child	No. of forms[a]	No. of Group items[b]	No. of Individual items
1	Pretest	28	28	1	28	0[c]
1	Posttest	84	21	4 × 4	44	40
2	Pretest	88	22	4 × 4	40	48
2	Posttest	125	25	5 × 5	50	75
3	Pretest[d]	125	25	5 × 5	50	75
3	Posttest	128	32	4 × 4	60	68
4	Pretest[e]	128	32	4 × 4	60	68
4	Posttest	144	36	4	0	144

[a] Number of **G** forms times number of **I** forms.
[b] See explanation in text.
[c] The pretest for Grade 1 was not based on matrix sampling.
[d] Substantially the same as the posttest for Grade 2.
[e] Identical to the posttest for Grade 3.

Test Construction

The validity of the evaluation of a curriculum project depends heavily on the appropriateness of the tests used to assess achievement. After reviewing 26 major curriculum-reform projects, Walker and Schafferzick (1974) concluded that an assessment of the effectiveness of a program depends strongly on the character of the test used in the assessment. Thus, when "traditional" tests (in particular, standardized tests) are used to compare an innovative program with a traditional program, the students in the traditional program usually score higher. In contrast, when the test is designed to measure achievement of the objectives of the innovative program, the students in the innovative program usually perform better than do students in the traditional program.

In light of these results, we considered it crucial to design tests that evaluated fairly the attainment of the skills and concepts being taught in both the Radio Mathematics program and the traditional mathematics program in Nicaragua. We addressed these concerns in several ways.

First, we viewed our task as designing a new instructional system, not constructing a new curriculum. We based the content of the radio lessons at each grade level on the curriculum guide prepared by the Nicaraguan Ministry of Public Education. We reorganized the presentation of the topics, spreading instruction on a topic over a longer period than that suggested by the Ministry guide. For Grades 1 and 2, the radio lessons covered most of the material in the curriculum guides; this was less true in Grades 3 and 4, as discussed in chapter 2.

We know which topics were taught by radio lessons; we have little direct knowledge of what topics were taught in traditional classrooms. However, our observations and the reports of teachers and supervisors suggested that teachers usually follow the curriculum guides conscientiously. Both programs were intended to have the same mathematical content; to the extent that they did, this difficulty in designing appropriate tests was minimized.[2]

The method used to construct tests was designed to improve the fairness of the tests. It consisted of the following steps.

1. Write curriculum objectives for the entire instructional program for a grade, classifying the objectives by major topic (e.g., numeration, addition, subtraction).

2. Eliminate from consideration those objectives that cannot be tested with a written test (e.g., oral counting).

3. Design appropriate test items for each remaining objective.

4. Choose the number of test items for each topic roughly in proportion to the time allotted to that topic in the Ministry curriculum guide. (Thus, if numeration is allotted 10 of the 33 weeks in first grade, then approximately 30% of the items will test numeration concepts.)

5. Distribute the allotted number of items systematically among the testable objectives in the topic. We did not choose items at random (within a topic) but selected them to represent important skills and concepts. (Item choices also were constrained by the matrix-sampling design, in that some individual items had to have the same general oral instruction.)

In the early stages of the project, tests resulting from this procedure were reviewed by an independent advisory committee of Nicaraguan educators. At all grade levels, the tests contained some items sampling curriculum objectives that were included in the Ministry guide but were not taught by the project lessons.

All tests were first given in classrooms not otherwise involved in project activities. In each case, the students chosen for the pilot-testing were at an appropriate stage of schooling. Thus, pretests to be given at the beginning of the school year (except for Grade 1) were

---

[2] Another problem related to this issue, the differential development of test-taking skills, will be discussed in the section on test administration.

pilot-tested at the end of the preceding school year with students one grade-level lower. Similarly, students at the beginning of the next higher grade were chosen to pilot-test posttests.

We should note that our goal in constructing posttests was to design tests that represented fairly the curriculum content of the programs being examined, not to select items with particular characteristics—for example, a mean score of 50% correct. Thus, the distribution of items among topics was not changed as a result of pilot-testing. Rather, the pilot-testing indicated pauses that were incorrectly timed, instructions that were not clear, speech that was paced incorrectly, and other characteristics of item presentation that needed improvement.

Pretest for Grade 1

For the pretest for Grade 1, we modified the mathematics section of the Spanish version of the kindergarten-level *Test of Basic Experiences* (TOBE), published by CTB/McGraw-Hill. The TOBE test was chosen because it was available, covered appropriate material, and could be adapted with less effort than required to develop a new test. (We first used this pretest in February 1975, only a few months after we arrived in Nicaragua.)

The TOBE test booklet is made up of 28 pages, one item per page, with the questions read aloud. All questions are multiple choice with four illustrations. The children are instructed to make a mark through the illustration indicating their answer. Although the test format proved to be suitable for Nicaraguan first-grade students, many of the questions in the published test were not, either because the illustrations were unfamiliar (e.g., U.S. coins) or the language was unsuitable. Based on a critique of the test by Nicaraguan educators and on the results of our pilot-testing, changes were made in the oral component of about 20% of the items. (The illustrations in the printed booklet could not be changed, of course. The picture of coins was used to ask about relative sizes.)

Test Administration

We took care to standardize the conditions under which the project personnel administered the tests. For the project-designed tests, a standard set of instructions was tape recorded and played in classrooms on cassette recorders. (The posttest for Grade 4 did not require taped instructions, because all instructions were printed.) Early project work investigated appropriate designs for major test components—the answer sheets, the oral instructions directing students to the proper place on their answer sheets, and the wording of

112   SEARLE AND GALDA

test items. This work was particularly important in Nicaragua, because students have little experience taking tests with printed test
papers. Although the tests were paced by the taped instructions,
ample time was allowed for students to respond. The staff administering the tests reported that only rarely were students handicapped
by lack of time. Nicaraguan educators checked the printed portions of
test items to make sure that the exercise formats would be familiar to
students. In short, we invested substantial effort in producing tests
that were understood by and acceptable to all children.

Children who listen to radio lessons for a year are likely to be
familiar with the testing situation because of the practice they receive
in responding to recorded instructions. This experience may give
them an advantage over children from traditional classes. We tried to
minimize this by the care with which test instructions were written and
with pilot tests with inexperienced children. We think that the children in control classes coped well with the tests, and we can provide
some empirical evidence to support this belief. All project tests contained at least one item in the body of the test (i.e., not one of the first
items) for which the mean percentage correct for students with no
radio experience was at least 95, suggesting that most students understood the mechanics of the testing procedure well enough to keep
pace with the oral instructions and to respond in the proper place on
the test paper.

2. METHODS FOR ANALYZING TEST RESULTS

Three methods were used to analyze test results. Detailed comparisons of instructional methods were made based on test-item scores. A
method of estimating total test scores with matrix-sampling designs
reported by Sirotnik (1975) was applied to compare treatments with
the classroom as the unit of analysis. Finally, estimated student scores
were used to compare performance of subgroups of students.

Item Scores

Because we used matrix sampling to design the tests, we had to
look beyond the customary method of analyzing test scores—namely,
working with means of scores attained by individual students. Over
the years, the project has reported mean item scores for groups of
students and has based its assessment of treatment effects on differences between means of item means (see Searle, Suppes, & Friend,
1976; Suppes, Searle, & Friend, 1978). In this chapter we again use
item scores but take a slightly different approach. Because each item
was given to both groups, we have a natural pairing of scores, which

enables us to compute score differences for each item. Instead of comparing the sample of experimental item scores with the sample of control item scores, we examine the sample of item-score differences. We focus on the mean of this sample and test whether it is significantly different from zero. We believe that the population of item-score differences is the real quantity of interest here. Furthermore, tests of significance will be more decisive in this one-sample analysis, because taking differences eliminates the variation due simply to item difficulty.

Figures 3 and 4 illustrate the kinds of data we are dealing with. Figure 3 presents the distribution of item scores for the 1976 first-grade posttest, plotting results for experimental and control classes separately. The figure shows the number of test items with scores falling in each score decile. Figure 4 presents the distribution of score differences for the same data. The differences (experimental less control) range from −17 to 64 percentage points. Note that both figures illustrate the superior performance of the experimental group over the control group; Figure 4 points out perhaps more dramatically the consistency of this superiority.

Estimated Total-test Scores

A method for analyzing scores obtained from matrix-sampling tests has been reported by Sirotnik (1975). This method was adapted and extended to apply to project data by Wagner (1978). The purpose

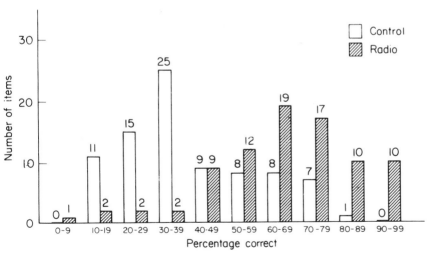

FIGURE 3. Distribution of item scores for experimental and control groups, Grade 1, 1976.

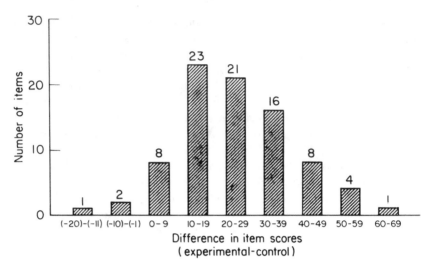

FIGURE 4. Distribution of the difference of item scores (experimental less control) for Grade 1, 1976 data.

of Sirotnik's method is to estimate the group mean and variance that would have been observed if each of the N students had taken all M items of the test under consideration. Briefly, the group mean is estimated by the actual, observed mean. The variance of this mean is estimated from components of variance for students, items, and error, which are obtained from estimates of mean squares in the classical manner (Cornfield & Tukey, 1956).

For purposes of analysis, each project test is composed of two matrix-sampling tests, one consisting of all **G** items, another of all **I** items. Sirotnik's method estimates means and variances for these separately; they were combined to produce an overall estimate. Wagner's extension considers generalization of results along two dimensions, to the relevant population of students and to the relevant population of test items—that is, arithmetic at the appropriate grade level. Wagner's method allows computation of the appropriate statistics with either the student or the class as the unit of analysis. Because random assignment to treatment was made at the classroom level, it is appropriate to analyze the test results with the class as the unit of analysis. This has not been done for all the evaluations reported, because in some cases data were not collected in such a way as to allow these analyses to be carried out.

Estimated Student Test Scores

Subsequent to choosing matrix-sampling test designs, it became clear to us that many questions of interest could be investigated only by being able to match pretest and posttest scores of individual students. We therefore adopted a method for constructing estimated scores that is based on work by Kleinke (1972). A literature review of potential methods and a justification for adopting the procedure suggested by Kleinke are presented in Appendix C of Searle et al. (1976). We briefly summarize the method here, using for illustrative purposes the 1976 first-grade posttest, which has four **G** forms and four **I** forms. A total score on the test would consist of the sum of eight subtest scores. Each student completes a test paper with two parts, one **G** form and one **I** form. Thus, in order to obtain a total score, scores for six subtests must be estimated. Once this is done, an estimated total score is obtained by summing eight scores: the two actual scores attained by the student and the six estimated scores.

Kleinke's method for estimating the score on a single subtest, illustrated with **G** forms, is as follows. Let

X be the score on the **G** form the student took,
$\bar{X}$ be the mean score on this form for all students taking the form (experimental and control),
S_x be the standard deviation for this form,
Y be the score to be estimated (on another **G** form),
$\bar{Y}$ be the mean score on that **G** form, and
S_y be the standard deviation for that form.

Then

$$Y = \bar{Y} + \frac{S_y}{S_x}(X - \bar{X}).$$

The score obtained for each student is entirely a function of the standardized scores of the subtests taken by the student. Suppose a student took **G**-form A. His scores on **G**-forms B, C, and D must be estimated. The method assigns the score on B that is in the same position on the B distribution as the student's score on the A distribution, in units of standard deviations. Thus, if the student received a standard score of 1 on **G**-form A, he is given the score on **G**-form B that corresponds to a standardized score of 1. (Similarly for the C and D and **I** forms.) The procedure can be seen most clearly for a student whose scores on the subtests he or she took are in fact the mean scores for the students who took those forms. This student's estimated total score is the sum of the mean scores for each subtest.

The student scores estimated by the Kleinke method are used in regression analyses presented later in this chapter. They have also been used in other project investigations: See Jamison, 1978; Searle,

Sheehan, González, and George, 1978; and chapters 5 and 7 of this volume. For some of the analyses, estimated scores have been aggregated to the classroom level.

3. EVALUATION DESIGN AND IMPLEMENTATION

Each year the project worked with schools and classes that played different roles, were chosen in different ways, and can be classified as receiving different treatments. These are summarized in Figure 5. Two treatments, *radio-experimental* and *control*, were used for summative evaluation; the *radio-observed* treatment was used for formative evaluation (see chap. 3); and the *radio-volunteer* treatment was used to satisfy a project commitment to teachers of other classes in radio schools.

Assigning Classes to Treatments

The first step in assigning classes to treatments was to designate schools as potentially radio or control. Assignments were made according to schools rather than classes for several reasons. First, children are likely to overhear radio lessons from other classrooms, since school buildings are often not well constructed (some are converted private homes) and classrooms are poorly separated. Second, many

Radio—Experimental: Classes were randomly selected, teachers were asked to use radio lessons, classes were not observed, and students were pretested and posttested for summative evaluation.

Radio—Observed: Classes were systematically selected to be representative, were observed and tested frequently during the school year, and were pretested and posttested, but results were *not* used for summative evaluation.

Radio—Volunteer: Classes were in radio schools taught by teachers who had used the radio lessons previously and chose to continue, and these classes were pretested and posttested as resources permitted, but results were *not* used for summative evaluation.

Control: Classes were randomly selected, were pretested and posttested for summative evaluation, but were not observed.

FIGURE 5. Project treatments.

students are not promoted, so that classes do not remain intact.[3] Thus, children in control classes in schools where others were following the radio lessons would very likely hear the lessons, thereby contaminating the treatment. We have some evidence that in later years some teachers in control schools used radio lessons (see chap. 8), but for the most part the distinction was maintained.

School populations were stratified along two dimensions, namely, province and urbanization. The project worked in schools in three provinces—Masaya, Carazo, and Granada—and recognized two levels of urbanization—urban and rural. At the outset of project work in an area, schools were designated as radio or control by the following procedure.

1. All schools with fewer than 15 students in first grade were eliminated from consideration.

2. Using the Ministry of Education designations for urban and rural, lists of urban and rural schools were drawn up.

3. Within each list, each school was randomly designated (with probability .5) as potentially radio or control.

This designation remained in force until 1978. By then, the list of radio schools in some strata was depleted. Furthermore, radio classes with no prior radio experience were needed. Therefore, the schools designated as control but not being used for that purpose in 1978 were added to the pool of possible radio schools prior to the further selection procedures described below.

Selecting classes for summative evaluation. If the curriculum for a particular grade level was to be evaluated during a year, then two groups of classes, designated experimental and control, were chosen from radio and control schools, respectively, using a random-selection procedure with three steps.

1. The number of classes to be chosen from each stratum was determined.

2. For each cell in the stratification (e.g., rural, control schools in Masaya), a list was prepared of all eligible classrooms.

3. The appropriate number of classes was selected at random from each list.

At each grade level, equal numbers of classes were chosen from each province. For Grades 1 and 2, the ratio of urban to rural classrooms

---

[3] While some students transfer from one school to another, this does not appear to happen frequently. No attempt was made to follow the histories of individual children in this regard.

was 1:1; for Grades 3 and 4 this ratio was 3:5.[4] More rural classrooms were selected at the higher grades to attempt to equalize the sizes of the populations, since at higher grade levels, rural classes typically are smaller than urban classes. In most cases, at least 20, and sometimes as many as 30, classes were chosen for each treatment. Frequently, fewer control classes than experimental classes were tested because we wanted to estimate the performance of experimental classes with greater precision than we did performance of control classes. For example, the sample for the summative evaluation of Grade 1 in 1976 consisted of five experimental and four control classes for each of the six cells formed from three provinces and two levels of urbanization (Masaya-urban, Masaya-rural, etc.), a total of 30 experimental classes and 24 control classes.

The schools in the experimental area are typical of most Nicaraguan public schools. Much of Nicaragua is a similar mixture of provincial towns of from 15,000 to 80,000 people surrounded by rural areas whose populations live fairly close to the towns. The exceptions are the capital city of Managua, with a population of 500,000, and the sparsely populated area on the eastern coast, where about 10% of the population lives. We believe the experimental results obtained in the three provinces can be generalized to all of Nicaragua except for the area around Managua and the area on the eastern coast.

Selecting classes for formative evaluation. During the year that the radio lessons for a grade were being developed, a group of classes was selected to provide feedback to curriculum developers. These classes, the radio-observed classes, although not selected at random for logistic reasons, were sampled to represent the range of conditions likely to be found in schools in the rural areas and small towns of Nicaragua. The children in these classes were given not only pretests and posttests but were also tested regularly throughout the year. In addition, the classrooms were observed on a regular basis. This work is reported in chapter 3 and in Galda and de Quintanilla (1978).

Selecting volunteer classes. Many teachers whose classes had been selected to participate either as experimental or as observed classes wanted to continue using the radio lessons in subsequent years. Wherever possible, the project encouraged them to do so and provided the necessary materials. Teachers of other grades in schools working with the project could also use lessons upon request if arrangements could be made. When resources permitted, the children in these classes were pretested and posttested, but the results are not reported here.

---

[4] This change in ratio was adopted in 1977. The third-grade control group, which was tested in 1976, contained equal numbers of rural and urban schools.

In the period from 1975 to 1978 the project worked with about 600 radio classes and 145 control classes, as shown in Table 2. The number of volunteer classes increased steadily, reaching 213 in 1978.

Experimental Design for Summative Evaluation

The first summative evaluations of project lessons were conducted in 1976 for first grade and in 1977 for second grade. Beginning with

TABLE 2

Distribution of Classes Cooperating with Project

Grade	Number of control classes	Number of radio classes			
		Experimental	Observed	Volunteer	Total
		1975			
1	9	16[a]	11	6	33
		1976			
1	24	30	11	15	56
2	24	22	5	20	47
3	24	0	0	0	0
		1977			
2	0	42	0	13	55
3	0	24	12	24	60
4	24	0	0	0	0
		1978			
1	20	48	0	34	82
2	20	21	0	88	109
3	0	24	0	58	82
4	0	30	11	33	74
TOTAL	145	257	50	291	598

[a] This group of radio classes was not randomly selected.

third grade, a new strategy was adopted. To eliminate the possibility that students in control classes had listened to radio lessons, these classes were tested in the year prior to lesson production. Thus, the third-grade control classes were tested in 1976 and fourth-grade control classes in 1977. In one case, for second grade in 1977, a posttest-only comparison is presented because pretests were not administered. Finally, in 1978, at the third-grade level, only experimental classes were tested. These students were studied to examine the effect of prior radio experience on achievement; a control group was not necessary for this purpose.

The four evaluation designs described here are represented in Figure 6, using the notation of Campbell and Stanley (1963). Table 3 identifies the design employed in each of the comparisons.

Political Context of the Experiment

The Radio Mathematics Project carried on its work in Nicaragua from mid-1974 until January 1979. Before and during that period, significant changes took place in Nicaragua that, beyond question, influenced the operation of the project. In 1972, Managua, the capital city, suffered a severe earthquake that destroyed many homes. In 1974, many refugees from Managua were living in Masaya, the town in which the project had its headquarters. In the following years, many of these people moved back to Managua as new housing was built there. We have no data on the extent of this migration and are unable to determine whether it had an effect on the schools with which the project worked.

		Year $Y - 1$	Year Y
Design A:	R		$O_3 \quad O_4$
	R		$O_3 \times O_4$
Design B:	R	$O_1 \quad O_2$	
	R		$O_3 \times O_4$
Design C:	R		O_4
	R		$\times O_4$
Design D:	R		$O_3 \times O_4$

R : Random selection of test units.
O_i : Observation point i.
$\times$: Treatment.

FIGURE 6. Experimental designs used for summative evaluation.

TABLE 3

Experimental Designs for Comparing Curriculums

Grade	Year experimental group tested (Y)	Year control group tested	Design[a]
1	1976	1976	A
1	1978	1978	A
2	1977	None	C
2	1978	1978	A
3	1977	1976	B
3	1978	1976	D
4	1978	1977	B

[a] See Figure 6 for explanation of "Y" and design types.

Much more disruptive of project efforts was the revolution, which took place during most of 1978 (and a good part of 1979, as well). During the year, fighting shifted from one community to another. From the project's point of view, the major effects were closed schools or, alternatively, shortened school days, and lowered school attendance, because parents were afraid to let their children walk in the streets. Schools were closed officially only for short periods of time (two weeks at most). However, for substantial periods, many of the schools closed in mid-morning. This meant that fourth-grade students were not able to listen at school to the radio mathematics lessons, which were broadcast at 11:00 A.M. The lessons were broadcast almost every day during the year, even when schools were known to be closed. We do not know how many children listened to lessons at home, although we know that some did so (see chap. 8).

Although the staff had contingency plans to evacuate, the plans were never put into effect, and data collection continued until close to the end of the school year. (Posttests were administered two weeks earlier than they had been scheduled.) As noted in Table 3, Grades 1 and 2 were evaluated for a second time in 1978, allowing a comparison of results for years with and for those without political turmoil. This interesting comparison is reported in a later section.

4. RESULTS

The work reported here addresses the major evaluation question—Do students using radio lessons perform significantly better than students in traditional classrooms on a test of mathematics achievement?—as well as several other questions of interest. Among these are the following.

— How does performance compare on topics that were taught and on those that were not taught by radio lessons?

— Does performance of students in urban and rural areas differ?

— What is the effect on mathematics achievement of using radio lessons for more than one year?

— Do boys and girls perform differently on mathematics achievement tests?

— Are achievement gains found for students of all ability levels?

— Are higher achievement levels in mathematics attained at the expense of achievement in other school subjects?

Cronbach (1976) and others have argued persuasively that in educational settings where classes rather than students are assigned at random to treatments, the analysis of performance data should take the class as the unit of analysis. The analysis methods described earlier, designed to handle data from matrix-sampling tests (Sirotnik, 1975; Wagner, 1978), allow us to compare performance of experimental and control classes and thus to answer the major evaluation question we have posed. However, they do not permit calculation of mean scores for individual classes (or students) and are therefore not suitable for examining the other questions of interest. Thus, once we present the major comparison of posttest scores, we turn to subsidiary analyses using item scores and estimated student scores.

Comparison of Experimental and Control Groups

Table 4 reports posttest comparisons for four grade levels, applying the methods of Wagner (1978) and Sirotnik (1975) described earlier with the classroom as the unit of analysis. The results demonstrate the superior performance of experimental over control classes for Grades 1 through 3. Scores for fourth-grade experimental and control classes are not significantly different. The following sections explore these results further.

Numbers of Students in Experimental and Control Groups

Table 5 presents the numbers of students tested for the comparisons presented below. In Grades 1 and 2, about 20% fewer children were posttested than pretested. The decreases for Grades 3 and 4 are somewhat less, about 10% to 15%. However, the shifting in the population tested is much greater than suggested by Table 5. Thus, for example (see Table 6), of the 2,298 Grade 1 students who in 1978 took either the pretest or the posttest, 1,013 took the pretest only, 708

TABLE 4

Comparison of Posttest Scores for Experimental
and Control Classrooms

Grade	Year[a]	Experimental			Control			t
		Number of classes	Mean % correct	SD	Number of classes	Mean % correct	SD	
1	1976	30	65.4	3.9	23	38.8	5.4	20.83*
2	1977	40	66.1	5.5	24	58.4	6.3	5.13*
3	1977	24	51.7	8.9	24	43.2	6.6	3.76*
4	1978	29	34.7	8.6	19	33.8	8.7	.35

* $p < .01$.
[a] Year experimental group was tested; see Table 3 for year control group was tested.

TABLE 5

Numbers of Students Tested

Grade	Year[a]	Experimental		Control[b]	
		Pretest	Posttest	Pretest	Posttest
1	1976	696	571	564	438
1	1978	1,108	924	482	362
2	1978	440	344	398	338
3	1977	467	418	546	459
3	1978	420	377	-	-
4	1978	486	450	318	283

[a] Year experimental group was tested; see Table 3 for year control group was tested.
[b] No third-grade control group was tested in 1978.

took the posttest only, and only 577 took both tests. A major reason for the small proportion taking both tests is that test administrators were instructed to relieve overcrowding in classrooms (and resultant copying) by excusing students from tests. The rule followed was to limit the number of students to 30 in urban classrooms and 20 in rural classrooms by systematically excusing every nth child, where n was chosen to bring the numbers down to the required limit. It was impracticable to identify for posttesting those students who had taken the pretest, so that some children who were pretested may have been present for the posttest but excused (and similarly for children post-tested but not pretested).

Student dropout also accounts for some of the loss of students between pretest and posttest. Within-year dropout is greater in the early grades and decreases thereafter. Countering this trend, some students enter school during the second month. (These trends are documented in Searle, Sheehan, González, & George, 1978; Jamison, 1978; and chaps. 5 and 7 of this volume.)

Table 6 presents separately the pretest scores for students who did and who did not take the posttest, for several grade levels. Except for the first-grade control group, students who did not take the posttest scored lower on the pretest than those who took the posttest. Although the attrition appears to have affected the experimental and control groups slightly differently in Grade 1, these differences do not account for even a small part of the eventual differences found in posttest score between experimental and control groups, as will be seen later (in Table 9 below).

Comparisons of Treatment Groups Based on Item Scores

Pretest. Table 7 presents pretest results for four grades, displaying mean item scores for experimental and control groups. The table also presents the mean difference in item scores, as described earlier, as a measure of performance difference between treatment groups. Two different values for N are reported, which needs explanation. Looking at the third line, results for Grade 2, 1978, 110 is the mean number of students taking each item in the test. (Recall that each student took one-fourth of the items.) For the control group, the mean number of students taking each item was 99. The N used for testing the significance of the difference, reported in the seventh column of the table, was the number of items in the test.

Significant differences in pretest between experimental and control groups occur in three cases—Grade 1 in 1976 and Grades 3 and 4 in 1978. As we discuss below, the differences for Grades 3 and 4 reflect the inclusion in the samples of children with previous exposure

TABLE 6

Estimated Pretest Scores of Students Taking and
of Students Not Taking Posttest

Group	Pretest only			Both pretest and posttest		
	N	Mean	SD	N	Mean	SD
1978 Grade 1						
Control	317	79.0	15.9	165	77.2	17.4
Experimental	696	76.6	17.3	412	80.2	13.9
1977 Grade 3						
Control	164	59.4	10.9	382	61.6	10.0
Experimental	154	59.3	10.8	313	61.9	10.3
1978 Grade 4						
Control	105	47.1	8.8	213	49.1	8.6
Experimental	201	49.6	8.0	285	50.6	8.0

to radio mathematics lessons.[5] The difference for Grade 1, about .6 items on the 28–item test, has no obvious explanation.

The first-grade pretest scores differed substantially for the two years reported. The mean score for all students in 1976 was 73.7%; in 1978, 78.0%. This difference is statistically significant ($t = 6.78$, $p < .001$). The pretest was administered also in 1975 to 800 students (in classrooms that were not randomly selected); the mean score that year was 71.9%. Interestingly, there seems to be a trend toward higher pretest scores in Grade 1, amounting to about 2 percentage points a year. Whether this can be attributed to the presence of the project in the area (e.g., because children listened to radio programs at home) or to other factors, we have no way of knowing.

Posttest. Posttest scores for four grades are presented in Table 8. The differences between experimental and control groups are significant at the .001 level for all comparisons except fourth grade. That is, mean item-scores for students in Grades 1 through 3 studying

---

[5] Pretest scores for the subset of students without prior experience with radio lessons are comparable to those for control students. Compare Table 7 with Table 14 (shown later).

TABLE 7

Comparison of Pretest Item Means
for Experimental and Control Groups

		Experimental		Control		Experimental − Control		
Grade	Year[a]	Mean N[b]	Mean item score, % correct	Mean N	Mean item score, % correct	N[c]	Mean difference	SD[d]	t
1	1976	696[e]	74.7	564	72.4	28	2.3	3.7	3.27*
1	1978	1,139	77.9	481	78.3	28	.4	-	-
2	1978	110	57.1	99	56.5	88	.6	10.4	.55
3	1977	93	60.9	109	61.1	125	−.2	9.6	−.22
3	1978	84	65.5	109	61.1	125	4.4	10.3	4.77**
4	1978	121	51.1	79	47.8	128	3.3	10.2	3.68**

* $p < .01$.
** $p < .001$.
[a] Year experimental group was tested; see Table 3 for year control group was tested.
[b] Mean number of students who took each item.
[c] Number of items in the test.
[d] Pretest data for Grade 1, 1978, were not keypunched and were summarized by student, not item. Thus, we cannot calculate the standard deviation for scores summarized by item. (The overall means are the same for items and for students.)
[e] All students took all items on the Grade 1 pretest.

mathematics by radio were higher by from 6.6 to 24.8 percentage points than scores for control students.

The results presented in Table 8 allow several comparisons between 1978 and earlier years. Because of the political disturbances, we expected the posttest scores for 1978 to be much lower than those for earlier years. In fact, they are not. The largest mean difference is 4 percentage points, and that was an increase, rather than a decrease (Grade 1 control). This very surprising result was investigated further by regression analysis of the data for Grade 1. The analysis used estimated student scores, rather than item scores, to allow matching of pretest and posttest scores for individual students. (The regression analysis also takes into account the difference in pretest scores found in the 1976 first-grade data.) The results are presented in Table 9. The regression coefficients for all variables are significantly different from zero. The amount of posttest-score difference attributable to **YEAR** is quite small, an average decrease from 1976 to 1978 of 1.2 items in total posttest score (for an individual student) as compared

TABLE 8

Comparison of Posttest Item Means
for Experimental and Control Groups

Grade	Year[a]	Experimental		Control[b]		Experimental − Control			
		Mean N^c	Mean item score, % correct	Mean N	Mean item score, % correct	N^d	Mean difference	SD	t
1	1976	142	65.6	109	40.8	84	24.8	15.0	15.17*
1	1978	231	62.6	90	44.8	84	17.8	11.6	14.10*
2	1977	157	65.8	108	59.3	125	6.6	10.4	7.06*
2	1978	68	66.9	67	56.1	125	10.9	13.6	8.98*
3	1977	104	52.8	115	43.6	128	9.2	15.4	6.73*
3	1978	94	53.5	-	-	128	9.8[e]	16.5	6.74*
4	1978	112	34.5	71	34.1	144	.4	9.8	.43

* $p < .001$.
[a] Year experimental group was tested; see Table 3 for year control group was tested.
[b] No third-grade control was tested in 1978.
[c] Mean number of students who took each item.
[d] Number of items in the test.
[e] Comparison uses earlier control group data.

TABLE 9

Effect of Operational Year on Impact of Radio Instruction
and Other Variables on Posttest Score:
1976 and 1978, Grade 1

Independent variable	Regression results	
	B	t
RADIO	13.80	22.96
PRETEST	1.38	20.25
URBAN	2.88	4.72
YEAR	−1.22	2.09
Constant	8.91	
R^2	.47	

Note. YEAR = 0 for 1976, YEAR = 1 for 1978. The analysis used estimated student scores.

with a gain of 13.8 items attributable to the radio-lesson treatment. There was no evidence for a differential effect of **YEAR** on treatment groups; in a separate regression, the regression coefficient for an interaction term, **RADIO** × **YEAR**, was not significantly different from zero.

The posttest results for Grade 4 show no difference between control and experimental classes. Grade 4 lessons were developed and broadcast for the first time during 1978. As mentioned earlier, the evaluation for this grade level used a design in which the control group was tested in the year prior to implementation of the radio lessons. Even though the political turmoil apparently did not reduce test scores in Grades 1 through 3, the effect on Grade 4 remains an open question, because fourth-grade classes were particularly disrupted. As noted earlier, the fourth-grade lessons were broadcast at 11:00 A.M., which was approximately the time that schools closing early dismissed the children.

During 1978 the project conducted an experiment for the World Bank on the relative effectiveness of radio lessons and textbooks. This work is reported elsewhere (Jamison, Searle, Galda, & Heyneman, 1980), but we will discuss the test results for fourth-grade classes here for the light they shed on the control-experimental comparison.

One plan for exploring the control-experimental comparison further is to use the textbook group as a surrogate for a control group, making the assumption that a control group tested in 1978 would have scored no higher than the textbook group. (If the use of textbooks was effective in increasing student achievement, this would reduce the difference between the experimental and the textbook groups as compared with an appropriate control; consequently, the impact of radio lessons on test scores would be underestimated.)[6] The textbook experiment was run in the schools that had served as the 1977 control schools, so that students in the textbook group were quite comparable to those in the control group of the previous year. The control and textbook groups had the same scores on the pretest (47.8% and 47.5% correct, respectively), further substantiating their comparability. Thus, in several of the analyses that follow, we use the 1978 textbook as a surrogate control group.

Performance on items taught and not taught. Performance differences between experimental and control groups were explored further by placing posttest items in two groups—items that assess

---

[6] The textbook experiment was also conducted with Grade 1 students in 1978. At that grade level the difference between the control and textbook groups, both tested in 1978, was not statistically significant, suggesting that the impact of textbooks on achievement in this setting was small.

performance on concepts and skills taught by the radio programs, and all other test items. As the reader will recall, the posttest items were selected to represent all the topics included in the official curriculum guide, although not all these topics were taught by the radio programs. The proportion of topics taught by the radio programs is very high in the first two grades but decreases to about half in Grade 4 (see Table 10). The reasons for this decrease are discussed in detail in chapter 2. Briefly, only a portion of the material was covered, because both staff members and Ministry experts thought that too much material was included in the Ministry guides for Grades 3 and 4.

As is evident in Table 10, at all grade levels the experimental group performs substantially better than the control group on items taught by the radio lessons. (Note that the textbook group is used as a control for Grade 4.) For Grades 1 and 2, the experimental group also performs better than the control on items *not* taught by the radio lessons, but the difference is smaller than for items that are taught. Two further points of interest are illustrated in Table 10. First, the control group never performs better than the experimental group on items not taught by radio. Thus, it is difficult to argue that teachers of control classes are emphasizing different topics than are the radio lessons. Second, the performance levels in Grades 3 and 4 are very low for items not taught by radio. Apparently, no one is mastering these topics, which constitute one-third to one-half of the official curriculum.

These results help to interpret the score differences found at different grade levels. One effect of a larger number of items testing

TABLE 10

Comparison of Performance of Experimental and Control Groups on Posttest Items Taught and Not Taught by Radio

| Grade | % items taught | Mean percentage correct | | | | | |
| | | Items taught | | | Items not taught | | |
		Exp.	Cont.	Exp. − Cont.	Exp.	Cont.	Exp. − Cont.
1	89.3	68.6	42.1	26.6	40.8	30.3	10.5
2	93.6	67.6	56.2	11.3	58.0	53.6	4.4
3	73.8	63.9	51.3	12.6	24.7	24.6	.1
4[a]	52.1	49.1	41.3	7.8	18.6	18.3	.2

[a] Textbook group used instead of control group.

topics that have not been taught (and for which there is little or no score difference for the two groups) is to decrease the difference between overall posttest scores for these two groups. Thus, the higher percentage of items testing topics not taught on the tests for Grades 3 and 4 contributes to the smaller differences found between experimental and control groups at these grade levels.

Comparison of Performance in Urban and Rural Schools

Urban-rural differences have been documented in many primary-school systems. Typically, students in rural schools perform more poorly than those in urban areas. The results presented here suggest that this difference exists in Nicaragua and that, to some extent, the radio lessons helped rural students overcome this differential in performance.

Table 11 presents a comparison of pretest scores (using item means) of urban and rural students for three calendar years and four grade levels. Of the 12 comparisons presented, 10 either favor urban students or show no difference. The two cases in which rural students score higher than their urban counterparts—1978 experimental students in Grades 3 and 4—are instructive. In both cases, many of the students had participated in the radio lessons in previous years. Thus, the pretest scores probably reflect achievement levels attained through prior instruction by radio (discussed below).

Another urban-rural difference emerges from the table that is difficult to explain, but interesting nonetheless. In Grades 1 and 2, experimental students in rural areas score higher than control students. No comparable difference is found for urban students.

Table 12 compares the posttest scores (using item means) for students from urban and rural areas. Control students from rural areas consistently score lower than those from urban areas. For experimental students, the difference between urban and rural students is much reduced (and in a few cases reversed). However, as noted above, the pretest scores for experimental and control groups in the rural area are not the same. Thus, this difference is difficult to interpret. For Grade 3, where the pretest scores for experimental and control groups differ by less than one percentage point for both urban and rural students, and rural pretest scores are lower, the posttest results suggest that radio lessons are helping to close the gap between rural and urban students.

Effect of Prior Radio Experience

In 1978, the experimental classes at the third- and fourth-grade levels were chosen to include classes that had participated in radio

TABLE 11

Comparison of Pretest Scores
for Urban and Rural Students

Group	Urban		Rural	
	Mean % correct[a]	SD	Mean % correct	SD
Grade 1				
1976 control	73.9	17.1	70.3	20.4
1976 experimental	74.8	16.3	74.6	16.8
1978 control	80.3	13.8	75.2	19.5
1978 experimental	78.6	13.8	77.0	19.2
Grade 2				
1978 control	59.1	22.1	52.4	25.4
1978 experimental	58.7	19.5	55.3	21.3
Grade 3				
1976 control	62.5	23.7	58.5	24.6
1977 experimental	63.7	24.8	57.9	25.7
1978 experimental	64.9	24.1	65.9	23.6
Grade 4				
1977 control	48.3	28.3	47.4	27.9
1978 experimental	51.0	28.9	52.4	27.6
1978 textbook	48.9	29.0	45.4	28.5

[a] Computed with item means.

TABLE 12

Comparison of Posttest Scores
for Urban and Rural Students

Group	Urban		Rural	
	Mean % correct[a]	SD	Mean % correct	SD
Grade 1				
1976 control	44.6	20.9	34.3	22.1
1976 experimental	70.9	21.2	64.6	21.7
1978 control	49.3	22.1	38.3	21.4
1978 experimental	66.4	20.8	58.0	21.3
Grade 2				
1977 control	62.7	23.6	53.4	25.0
1977 experimental	66.0	21.8	65.3	22.8
1978 control	56.8	20.3	53.2	22.3
1978 experimental	66.5	19.4	67.3	20.5
Grade 3				
1976 control	45.6	26.5	41.9	27.2
1977 experimental	54.4	29.8	52.8	29.1
1978 experimental	53.2	27.9	54.2	20.5
Grade 4				
1977 control	35.0	27.5	33.0	26.0
1978 experimental	35.3	28.1	33.3	26.3
1978 textbook	29.2	26.7	31.3	25.6

[a] Computed with item means.

lessons in earlier years. The selections were based on the history of the class as a whole. This did not guarantee that each child in the class had taken part in the radio lessons before. On the contrary, because of dropout and repetition, the classes certainly contained students with different amounts of experience.

Pretest and posttest scores for classes with different levels of experience are presented in Table 13. Although the number of classes is small, the pattern of pretest results is consistent. Classes that have followed radio lessons in earlier years score higher than those that have not. The differences in posttest scores are small, although the ranking within grades is similar to that for the pretest.

The effect of prior experience was explored further by regression analysis with posttest score as the dependent variable and controlling for pretest score. There are three possible outcomes. If the regression coefficient for the variable **EXPERIENCE** is not different from zero, then posttest score is that which is predicted by pretest score alone

TABLE 13

Comparison of Test Scores for Classes
With and Without Prior Radio Experience

Years of prior experience	N	Pretest		N	Posttest	
		Mean % correct[a]	SD		Mean % correct[b]	SD
1978 Grade 3						
None	8	62.5	5.8	8	52.1	13.7
One	8	67.4	3.8	8	61.6	4.7
Two	7	65.2	5.6	7	54.7	5.5
1978 Grade 4						
None	8	49.5	4.5	7	32.1	5.8
One	11	51.5	4.6	11	33.6	8.5
Two	5	52.1	6.4	5	32.8	4.4
Three	6	55.6	1.8	6	37.1	4.7

[a] Estimated student scores aggregated by class.

[b] For Grade 3, mean percentage for I items, by class; for Grade 4, estimated student scores aggregated by class.

and, thus, classes with high pretest scores maintain their advantage. If the regression coefficient is greater than zero, classes with experience gain more than predicted by pretest scores alone. If the regression coefficient is less than zero, the classes have lost the advantage they started the year with. The results, presented in Table 14, suggest that the classes have at least maintained the advantage of experience that they had at the pretest (since the regression coefficient is not significantly different from zero).

We conclude from these results, which are only suggestive (because of the small number of classes and uncertainty about the histories of individual children), that students with prior radio experience have retained more mathematics from previous years than students without prior experience. They maintain this advantage throughout the year during which both groups listen to radio lessons.

Sex Differences in Mathematics Achievement

Sex differences in mathematics achievement are frequently found at the elementary-school level. Therefore, it was of interest to compare the performance of Nicaraguan boys and girls. The results appear in Table 15, which presents mean estimated test scores, pooled across treatments. Where there is a performance difference, boys score higher than girls. The difference is greater at lower grade levels and on pretests as compared with posttests.

In a regression analysis of the data for Grade 1, we found that sex was not a significant predictor of posttest score. (That is, the regression coefficient for this variable was not different from zero.) Since

TABLE 14

Effect of Experience on Posttest Score
Adjusted for Pretest Score:
Grade 3, 1978

Independent variable	Regression results	
	B	t
PRETEST	1.28	4.40
EXPERIENCE[a]	1.34	.42
Constant	−28.25	
R^2	.54	

[a] **EXPERIENCE** = 1 if class had prior experience with radio lessons.

TABLE 15

Comparison of Mathematics Achievement Scores of Boys and Girls

Test and year	Boys			Girls			t
	N	Mean % correct[a]	SD	N	Mean % correct	SD	
Grade 1							
1976 Pretest	518	77.5	16.1	436	71.8	16.4	5.40***
1978[b] Pretest	1,053	79.7	16.4	1,023	77.1	16.7	3.68***
1976 Posttest	456	57.4	17.5	426	53.5	18.0	3.26**
1978[b] Posttest	830	56.4	14.1	869	54.5	14.1	2.78**
Grade 2							
1976 Pretest	358	63.3	10.5	418	60.9	11.3	3.05**
1976 Posttest	332	64.2	8.7	380	63.4	9.0	1.20
Grade 3							
1977 Pretest	495	61.7	10.5	518	60.3	10.3	2.14*
1977 Posttest	412	50.0	8.1	465	49.2	8.7	1.40
Grade 4[b]							
1978 Pretest	567	49.2	8.1	597	49.0	8.1	.42
1978 Posttest	493	33.3	9.9	543	33.1	9.4	.33

* $p < .05$.
** $p < .01$.
*** $p < .001$.
[a] Computed with estimated scores.
[b] Includes textbook group.

boys and girls do not perform differently when pretest score is controlled for, the difference in posttest scores between boys and girls can be explained entirely by the differences in pretest scores. A search for an interaction between sex and treatment found none; boys and girls learn equally well from radio lessons.

Relation Between Score Gains and Pretest Score

Radio lessons, because they are broadcast to groups of children, cannot provide individualized instruction. Thus, there is a substantial risk that even when an instructional program can be shown to be effective—that is, mean achievement scores are raised—the gains will not be distributed equitably across students with different entering-skill levels. We investigated this question by dividing each group of students into thirds according to pretest score and looking at mean posttest scores for each of these subgroups. Table 16 shows typical results. For example, Grade 1 students whose pretest score is in the bottom third of the distribution show a mean posttest score of 55.6% for experimental students and 38.3% for control students. The difference between these is 17.3 percentage points. A similar difference between mean posttest scores is found for students in the middle and upper thirds of the distribution of pretest scores. Thus, radio lessons do not appear to serve students of one entering achievement level at the expense of others.

TABLE 16

Relationship Between Achievement Gains and Pretest Score

Score range on pretest	Mean percentage correct on posttest		
	Experimental	Control	Difference
1976 Grade 1			
Bottom third	55.6	38.3	17.3
Middle third	65.6	47.1	18.5
Top third	68.1	53.7	14.4
1977 Grade 3			
Bottom third	46.9	40.8	6.1
Middle third	53.2	47.6	5.6
Top third	57.6	53.0	4.6

Achievement in Other School Subjects

One possible explanation for higher mathematics achievement scores in experimental classes is that students are spending more time learning mathematics and less time on other subjects. If this were true, achievement levels in other school subjects would be expected to decline. Because no tests are administered regularly to Nicaraguan students, there were no relevant data available for testing this hypothesis. Designing a full testing program was beyond our resources; we restricted our effort to one grade level and one subject, Spanish.

We designed a test covering all of the material in the curriculum guide for second-grade language arts published by the Ministry of Public Education. The test was administered to all classes in the 1978 second-grade experimental and control groups at about the same time as the mathematics posttests. The results of this test are given in Table 17. There is no difference in performance of experimental and control groups on the language arts test, while the experimental group scored about 10 points higher on the mathematics achievement posttest (see Table 7, shown earlier). This result suggests that, at least with this group of students, the higher mathematics achievement scores were not gained at the expense of achievement in language arts.

5. CONCLUSIONS

The studies reported in this chapter addressed questions about the effectiveness of the Radio Mathematics Project lessons at four grade levels over a period of several years. We summarize here very briefly the results of these studies.

— At all grade levels, students learn the topics taught by the radio lessons better than students learn in traditional classrooms, as measured by a test of mathematics achievement.

TABLE 17

Results of 1978 Second-grade Spanish Test[a]

Group	No. of classes	No. of students	Mean % correct	SD
Control	20	348	59.5	27.2
Experimental	20	331	58.5	29.5

[a] 90 items, with each student taking 30.

— There is some evidence that radio lessons help rural students over-come the performance deficit they show compared to urban students.

— Students with radio experience score higher on mathematics achieve-ment tests given at the beginning of the year than do students without prior experience. This advantage is maintained during the school year.

— Radio mathematics lessons raise the mathematics achievement scores of students with low entering ability as much as those of students with high entering ability.

— Students studying mathematics by radio perform as well as traditional students on a language arts test, indicating that gains in mathematics achievement are not obtained at the expense of achievement in lan-guage arts.

— Boys and girls of equal ability learn equally well from radio lessons. In the lower primary grades, boys score higher on tests of mathematics achievement than do girls. Differences in posttest score are explained by differences in pretest score.

— Students attending school during a time of political turmoil show surprisingly small decreases in mathematics achievement scores, at all grade levels.

REFERENCES

Campbell, D., & Stanley, J. *Experimental and quasi-experimental designs for research*. Chicago: Rand McNally, 1963.

Cornfield, J., & Tukey, J. Average values of mean squares in factorials. *Annals of Mathematical Statistics*, 1956, **27**, 907–949.

Cronbach, L. *Research on classrooms and schools: Formulation of questions, design, and analysis* (Occasional Papers of the Stanford Evaluation Consortium). Stanford, Calif.: Stanford University, 1976.

Galda, K., & de Quintanilla, A. Weekly tests. In P. Suppes, B. Searle, & J. Friend (Eds.), *The Radio Mathematics Project: Nicaragua, 1976–1977*. Stanford, Calif.: Stanford University, Institute for Mathematical Studies in the Social Sciences, 1978.

Jamison, D. Radio education and student repetition in Nicaragua. In P. Suppes, B. Searle, & J. Friend (Eds.), *The Radio Mathematics Project: Nicaragua, 1976–1977*. Stanford, Calif.: Stanford University, Institute for Mathematical Studies in the Social Sciences, 1978.

Jamison, D., Searle, B., Galda, K., & Heyneman, S. *Textbook availability and school performance: An experiment from Nicaragua*. Unpublished manuscript, The World Bank, 1980.

Kleinke, D. A linear-prediction approach to developing test norms based on matrix-sampling. *Educational and Psychological Measurement*, 1972, **32**, 75–84.

Lord, F. Estimating norms by item sampling. *Educational and Psychological Measurement*, 1962, **22**, 259–267.

Lord, F., & Novick, M. *Statistical theories of mental test scores.* Reading, Mass.: Addison-Wesley, 1968.

Searle, B., Sheehan, J., González, J., & George, E. Patterns of promotion and wastage for Nicaraguan first-grade students. In P. Suppes, B. Searle, & J. Friend (Eds.), *The Radio Mathematics Project: Nicaragua, 1976-1977.* Stanford, Calif.: Stanford University, Institute for Mathematical Studies in the Social Sciences, 1978.

Searle, B., Suppes, P., & Friend, J. *The Radio Mathematics Project: Nicaragua, 1974-1975.* Stanford, Calif.: Stanford University, Institute for Mathematical Studies in the Social Sciences, 1976.

Shoemaker, D. Allocation of items and examinees in estimating a norm distribution by item-sampling. *Journal of Educational Measurement,* 1970, **7**, 123-128.

Shoemaker, D. A note on allocating items to subtests in multiple matrix sampling and approximating standard errors of estimate with the jacknife. *Journal of Educational Measurement,* 1973, **10**, 211-219.

Sirotnik, K. Introduction to matrix sampling for the practitioner. In W. Popham (Ed.), *Evaluation in education.* Berkeley, Calif.: McCutchan, 1975.

Suppes, P., Searle, B., & Friend, J. (Eds.). *The Radio Mathematics Project: Nicaragua, 1976-1977.* Stanford, Calif.: Stanford University, Institute for Mathematical Studies in the Social Sciences, 1978.

Wagner, W. *Application of matrix-sampling techniques to project achievement testing.* Unpublished manuscript, Stanford University, Institute for Mathematical Studies in the Social Sciences, 1978.

Walker, D., & Schafferzick, J. Comparing curricula. *Review of Educational Research,* 1974, **44**, 83-111.

As the last chapter showed, the radio mathematics lessons greatly improved the students' skills in mathematics. Although gains in achievement are the central issue here, there are several peripheral questions that this important outcome brings to mind. If the children learn more mathematics, is it possible that more of them will be promoted to the next grade? Certainly there are other school subjects that students must master, so promotion cannot depend entirely on mathematics; but even so, one might expect some increase in promotion rates due to improved performance in mathematics. In fact, failure in mathematics is often mentioned as one of the main causes for repetition. Attendance and dropout, also, are areas in which one might reasonably expect an improvement. If attendance and dropout are in any way related to either achievement or interest in school, then increased achievement and interest in mathematics due to improved instruction might have measurable effects there, too.

Promotion, attendance, and dropout are complex issues, however. There are many factors involved beyond simply those of curriculum design. Teachers influence all of these in various ways, and all teachers are not the same—in age, in experience, or in education. The social milieu, both in the school and in the larger community, may also be a factor. Larger classes may not have the same characteristics as smaller ones, rural schools certainly differ from urban ones, and schools so overcrowded they must have morning and afternoon shifts are different from schools where overcrowding is not a problem. And each child is an individual who differs from his companions in sex, age, and ability. Other factors in the child's life may also play a role. How far he needs to travel to school, the kind of work his parents do, and many other characteristics may play a role in determining his attendance patterns and his possibilities for promotion.

Some of these factors apply to classrooms as a whole (teacher characteristics, class size, etc.), while others apply to the individual student, which raises considerable theoretical difficulties for the statistician who wishes to study their combined effects on such outcomes as promotion and dropout and to sort out the differential effect of a special treatment (radio) from the background morass.

Ordinarily, statistical analysts of social science data get around the question of such complex interactions by assigning subjects randomly to experimental and control groups, so that the effects of background variables are felt equally by both groups, leaving the special treatment effect as the sole distinguishing characteristic.

In the case of the studies we conducted in the school system, however, such a solution was not feasible. In Nicaragua, classrooms could be chosen at random, but because of the established educational structure, students could not be assigned randomly to classrooms. The methodology developed and presented in this chapter was designed specifically to allow meaningful conclusions to be drawn about the differential influences of the treatment on the outcomes in question, given this limitation.

Chapter 5

EXPLORING THE EFFECTS
OF THE RADIO MATHEMATICS PROJECT
ON SCHOOL-RELATED VARIABLES

EDWARD I. GEORGE

THE PURPOSE OF THIS CHAPTER is to assess the relative effects of the Radio Mathematics Project lessons on the achievement, attendance, failure, dropout, and reenrollment of students in the first, second, and third grades in the context of numerous background variables. Our analysis derives its initial motivation from Jamison (1978), who evaluated the determinants of student failure and repetition using the 1975 first-grade data base of this project. (See chap. 7 for further comments by Jamison on the relation between radio lessons and student achievement and failure.) Recognizing an all-encompassing predictive recursive relationship among the variables studied, Jamison approximated these relationships with a large but unified linear predictive model that incorporated the effect of every variable considered relevant.[1] This model was fitted to the data and then used to compare the overall or average outcomes (achievement, attendance, failure, dropout, and reenrollment) for students who did and for those who did not participate in the radio instructional program.

We are concerned here not so much with predicting how a given population will fare but, rather, with explaining what part of the outcome is attributable to the project lessons. We have departed from Jamison's framework mainly because in such a large model it is extremely difficult to identify the unique and relative effects of any particular variable.

Simply stated, we will measure the size and direction of the effects of radio lessons compared to those of other variables. Our basic tools

The author wishes to thank Dean Jamison whose many ideas provided the impetus for this analysis. The work reported here was undertaken in part under the auspices of the World Bank.

[1] More precisely, Jamison used three linear models and three log-linear models.

are linear statistical methods, mainly multiple regression with an emphasis on variance-decomposition interpretation. Using an approach suggested by Wiley (1976), we attempt to disentangle the many sources of variance in our outcome variables. This involves an analysis-of-covariance type of adjustment for individual-level background variables, followed by a classroom-level analysis. We have restricted our search to the linear effects of the variables.[2]

1. THE DATA

The data base for our analysis consisted of observations from first, second, and third grade, all collected for the 1976 school year except for data from third-grade radio classes collected in 1977. A stratified random-sampling plan was used to collect the data. That is, a fixed number of classes was selected randomly from each of several representative strata. These classes were then randomly designated as experimental (radio) or control. A detailed discussion of this procedure is presented in chapter 4 of this volume. An important point to note here is that the basic sampling unit was the class and not the student. Thus, the randomization is not likely to eliminate initial differences between the classes. These class differences were a major consideration in carrying out the present analysis.

Table 1 lists the variables we considered in this analysis and presents the number of cases for which observations were available, along with means and standard deviations for each grade. For each variable, the number of observed values (N) in Table 1 is often substantially smaller than the total number of cases, shown in Table 2. This missing-value structure leads to large reductions in sample size in some of the multiple regression analyses because we require all variable values for every case.

The variables considered here fall into three categories—outcome variables, student background variables, and classroom background variables. The first two sets are defined for individuals, while the last set is defined for the class as a whole. Jamison (1978) used these same variables, as they appeared to be the most informative; however, he treated the classroom variables at the individual level by assigning their values to every individual in each class.

2. PRELIMINARY ANALYSIS

Perusal of the variable means in Table 1 yields some interesting

---

[2] The effect of a variable X on Y is linear if the relationship between X and Y can be expressed as $Y = BX + f(Z)$, where B is a constant (often referred to as the "effect" of X) and $f(Z)$ does not involve X.

TABLE 1

Variable Definitions and Descriptive Statistics

Variable	Definition	Grade	N	Mean	SD
	Outcome variables				
POST	Student's posttest score	1	882	46.67	14.97
	in mathematics	2	712	79.69	11.16
		3	558	63.24	10.66
ATTAV	Student's average	1	1,829	15.39	2.43
	attendance in days	2	1,224	16.03	1.85
	per month	3	859	15.61	2.12
FAIL	1 if student failed	1	1,956	.372	.484
	grade	2	1,257	.173	.378
		3	876	.177	.382
DROP	1 if student dropped	1	1,829	.144	.351
	out during school year	2	1,224	.049	.216
		3	859	.050	.218
RENRL	1 if student reenrolled	1	1,427	.924	.266
	in subsequent school	2	978	.907	.290
	year	3	648	.887	.316
	Student background variables				
MALE	1 for male student,	1	2,021	.538	.499
	0 for female	2	1,296	.469	.499
		3	963	.490	.500
AGE	Age of student,	1	1,950	8.52	1.79
	in years	2	1,290	10.04	1.81
		3	917	11.32	1.94
AGOCC	1 if student's family is	1	1,951	.306	.461
	employed in agriculture	2	1,245	.257	.437
		3	852	.275	.447
DIST	Distance in kilometers	1	1,595	.817	1.12
	of student from school	2	1,173	.913	1.72
		3	878	.854	1.03
NRPT	Number of times student	1	2,021	.515	.520
	repeated grade	2	1,296	.231	.569
		3	963	.300	.625
PRE	Student's pretest score	1	954	20.96	4.61
	in mathematics	2	776	54.61	9.18
		3	536	77.36	10.26

(TABLE 1, cont.)

Variable	Definition	Grade	N	Mean	SD
	Classroom background variables				
RURAL	1 if class in rural	1	52	.481	.504
	school	2	43	.511	.505
		3	38	.657	.480
USH	1 if class in urban	1	52	.307	.466
	school with shifts	2	43	.372	.489
		3	0		
UNOSH	1 if class in urban	1	52	.211	.412
	school without shifts	2	43	.116	.324
		3	38	.342	.480
CLSIZ	Student-to-teacher ratio	1	52	40.00	11.14
	of classroom	2	43	32.02	10.49
		3	38	25.39	12.68
RADIO	1 if class received	1	52	.576	.498
	radio instruction	2	43	.465	.504
		3	38	.473	.506
TAGE	Age of class's teacher,	1	52	30.54	10.05
	in years	2	43	28.81	14.53
		3	38	29.82	12.10
TED	Education of class's	1	52	10.96	2.07
	teacher, in years	2	43	8.67	5.26
		3	38	11.26	2.34
TEXP	Teaching experience	1	52	9.90	9.30
	of class's teacher,	2	43	10.98	10.50
	in years	3	38	11.13	8.12

overall grade-to-grade comparisons for some variables. (Unfortunately, the results for the variables **PRE** and **POST**—the students' pretest and posttest scores—are based on different scales across grades, thereby preventing comparison of the means.)[3]

Of the outcome variables, average attendance remained relatively stable from grade to grade. The numbers of students failing the grade and dropping out during the school year were stable in Grades 2 and 3, while two and three times smaller, respectively, than in

---

[3] These test scores are the means of estimated raw scores, as described in chapter 4.

TABLE 2

Overall Sample Sizes

Grade	Number of students	Number of classes		
		Total	Radio	Control
1	2,021	52	30	22
2	1,296	43	20	23
3	963	38	18	20

Grade 1. Reenrollment decreases as grade level increases, though not markedly, suggesting that between-year dropout tends to increase with grade level.

Of the student background variables, only the number of times the student repeated the grade shows substantial variation from grade to grade: Grade 1 is made up of students with longer repetition histories. Of the class-level variables, **RURAL** reflects the increased number of rural classes sampled in higher grades to make up for the decreasing class sizes in rural schools (see chap. 4). By the third grade, there are no urban classes that are taught in shifts (**USH**) in our sample. Class size (**CLSIZ**) decreases with increasing grade level. Teachers are younger (**TAGE**) and less experienced (**TEXP**) in the second grade, though the variability of these factors is also larger there. Finally, teachers with more experience teach the higher grades.

Table 3 compares the means for the radio and control subsamples and presents the two-sample t statistic and significance level for testing the hypothesis of equal means in the relevant population. Posttest scores (**POST**) were substantially higher in radio classes in all three grades. Attendance rates (**ATTAV**) in radio classes were lower for Grades 2 and 3. A higher proportion of radio students was failed (**FAIL**), although only in the first-grade sample is the difference of substantial statistical significance. Dropout rates (**DROP**) were higher in radio classes for Grades 1 and 2. Reenrollment rates (**RENRL**) for radio students were significantly smaller in Grades 2 and 3. A striking inconsistency here is that in spite of higher achievement-test scores, radio students were more often denied promotion.

If the radio and control classes were of the same makeup at the outset of the project, as we would like to have achieved with random-sampling techniques, then the statistical significance of the differences pointed out above would be reasonably conclusive. However, the significant differences between the subsample means of some of the

TABLE 3

Radio and Control Subsample Means and t Statistics

Variable	Grade	Subsample means		t	Significance level
		Control	Radio		
		Outcome variables			
POST	1	38.70	52.27	−14.81	.000
	2	75.91	84.26	−10.70	.000
	3	60.57	67.45	−7.83	.000
ATTAV	1	15.37	15.40	−.29	.774
	2	16.30	15.75	5.21	.000
	3	16.01	15.06	6.65	.000
FAIL	1	.337	.394	−2.53	.011
	2	.156	.191	−1.65	.100
	3	.157	.206	−1.89	.059
DROP	1	.103	.168	−3.79	.000
	2	.027	.072	−3.67	.000
	3	.056	.042	.96	.339
RENRL	1	.925	.923	.11	.914
	2	.928	.884	2.35	.019
	3	.914	.825	3.32	.001
		Student background variables			
MALE	1	.532	.542	−.42	.671
	2	.491	.444	1.68	.094
	3	.462	.532	−2.15	.032
AGE	1	8.87	8.30	6.83	.000
	2	9.89	10.20	−3.18	.002
	3	11.47	11.08	3.02	.003
AGOCC	1	.252	.338	−4.04	.000
	2	.213	.311	−3.95	.000
	3	.194	.384	−6.28	.000
DIST	1	.731	.872	−2.46	.014
	2	.861	.972	−1.10	.271
	3	.833	.886	−.75	.455
NRPT	1	.449	.554	−3.16	.002
	2	.188	.282	−2.98	.003
	3	.366	.202	4.04	.000
PRE	1	20.83	21.07	−.78	.435
	2	52.18	57.81	−8.89	.000
	3	77.84	76.62	1.35	.179

student background variables suggest a different makeup of the radio and control classes. Significant differences appear in the variables **AGE, AGOCC,** and **NRPT** in all three grades and in **DIST** and **PRE** in Grades 1 and 2, respectively. Thus, adjustments for background effects may well bear upon any conclusions about the effect of radio instruction.

3. ANALYSIS OF VARIANCE

The total variation of all the student-level variables is broken down into between-class and within-class components in an analysis of variance reported in Table 4.[4] Sizable F ratios in all but one case (first-grade **MALE**) strongly suggest class-level effects, that is, differences in class means attributable to more than student-to-student variation.[5] We report R^2 (the ratio of the between-class sum of squares to the total sum of squares), which is a measure of the size or degree of between-class variation, and the intraclass correlation coefficient, which is a measure of the proportion of total variance accounted for by class effects.[6] The discrepancy between these two measures is that portion of the between-class variation attributable to student-to-student variation.

For the outcome variables, the intraclass correlation coefficients provide an upper bound for the portion of the total variance that class-level variables might explain. For instance, although 34.6% of the variation in first-grade posttest scores occurs at the class level, at most 16.4% can effectively be explained or controlled by any set of our class background variables.

---

[4] We measure the total variation of the variable Y by the sum of squared deviations from the grand mean, that is, $SS_{total} = \sum_{ij}(Y_{ij} - Y_{..})^2$. We partition this into two components—the between-class sum of squares, $SS_{between} = \sum_i n_i(Y_{i.} - Y_{..})^2$ and the within-class sum of squares, $SS_{within} = \sum_{ij}(Y_{ij} - Y_{i.})^2$. Notice $SS_{total} = SS_{between} + SS_{within}$. Throughout this chapter, we have followed the convention that the first subscript i identifies classes, the second subscipt j identifies students within a class, I is the total number of classes, and n_i is the number of students in the ith class. Also we use the "." subscript to denote means, so that $Y_{i.} = \sum_j Y_{ij}/n_i$ and $Y_{..} = \sum_{ij} Y_{ij}/N$ where $N = \sum_i n_i$ is the total number of students.

[5] Under the assumption that our variables came from a normal distribution, every F ratio reported (except first-grade **MALE**) would be significant at the .001 level or smaller. However, in our analysis we will use most of the statistics as indices of importance rather than for hypothesis testing, thus avoiding the need for distributional assumptions.

[6] Each of our variables may be expressed as the sum of two components, $Y_{ij} = C_i + e_{ij}$, where the C_i are class effects and the e_{ij} are within-class effects. If the C_i are considered as random effects, the intraclass correlation coefficient $p = VAR(C)/VAR(Y)$, where VAR denotes the variance of the parent population.

TABLE 4

Analysis of Variance

Variable	Grade	Source of variation[a]	DF	Mean square	F	R^2	Intraclass correlation
			Outcome variables				
POST	1	B	51	1,338.973	8.61	.346	.164
		W	830	155.562			
	2	B	39	691.635	7.55	.305	.179
		W	672	91.561			
	3	B	31	580.005	6.73	.284	.184
		W	526	86.162			
ATTAV	1	B	48	112.503	36.90	.499	.481
		W	1,780	3.049			
	2	B	41	56.526	36.15	.556	.539
		W	1,182	1.564			
	3	B	33	69.170	36.57	.594	.583
		W	825	1.891			
FAIL	1	B	51	1.031	4.85	.115	.090
		W	1,904	.212			
	2	B	42	.430	3.23	.100	.069
		W	1,214	.133			
	3	B	36	.530	4.10	.150	.108
		W	839	.129			
DROP	1	B	48	.924	9.09	.197	.173
		W	1,780	.102			
	2	B	42	.127	2.91	.094	.060
		W	1,181	.044			
	3	B	33	.167	3.89	.135	.102
		W	825	.043			
RENRL	1	B	48	.606	11.66	.289	.215
		W	1,378	.052			
	2	B	38	.590	9.21	.272	.215
		W	939	.064			
	3	B	28	.355	4.00	.153	.106
		W	619	.089			

(TABLE 4, cont.)

Variable	Grade	Source of variation[a]	DF	Mean square	F	R^2	Intraclass correlation
		Student background variables					
PRE	1	B	51	54.063	2.79	.136	.044
		W	902	19.368			
	2	B	39	398.684	5.90	.238	.140
		W	736	67.574			
	3	B	31	357.938	3.98	.197	.105
		W	504	89.729			
MALE	1	B	51	.196	.78	.020	.000
		W	1,969	.250			
	2	B	42	1.135	5.17	.148	.122
		W	1,253	.220			
	3	B	37	.754	3.28	.116	.082
		W	925	.230			
AGE	1	B	50	30.340	12.15	.242	.223
		W	1,899	2.497			
	2	B	42	25.331	10.00	.252	.230
		W	1,247	2.533			
	3	B	35	21.519	7.02	.218	.191
		W	881	3.065			
AGOCC	1	B	50	5.005	58.09	.604	.595
		W	1,900	.086			
	2	B	42	2.951	31.16	.521	.501
		W	1,202	.095			
	3	B	33	2.497	23.39	.485	.468
		W	818	.107			
DIST	1	B	44	10.039	10.10	.223	.190
		W	1,550	.994			
	2	B	38	11.213	4.21	.124	.096
		W	1,134	2.664			
	3	B	35	3.625	3.82	.137	.100
		W	842	.950			

(TABLE 4, cont.)

Variable	Grade	Source of variation[a]	DF	Mean square	F	R^2	Intraclass correlation
NRPT	1	B	51	5.050	12.53	.245	.229
		W	1,969	.403			
	2	B	42	1.484	5.22	.149	.123
		W	1,253	.284			
	3	B	37	1.714	5.07	.169	.138
		W	925	.338			

[a] B = between class; W = within class.

Except for **ATTAV**, by far the greatest proportion of the variance of the outcome variables lies within classes. The intraclass correlations are relatively stable for each variable over grades, so that any observable trends, such as increasing **POST** class variation, are probably unimportant. The variable **ATTAV** exhibits the largest degree of between-class variation, more than 50% in Grades 2 and 3. One explanation for this might be artificially stable attendance data in each class, causing abnormally small within-class variation.[7] At the other extreme, we find little between-class variation in all grades for **FAIL**, in Grades 2 and 3 for **DROP**, and in Grade 3 for **RENRL**, suggesting that class characteristics may be ineffective in explaining the variation of these variables. That posttest scores vary so much more between classes than do failure rates is disturbing and suggests that student achievement in mathematics, as measured by the posttest score, may not be a basic criterion for student failure. This observation is borne out in our later analysis, as well as in chapters 6 and 7 of this volume and in Searle, Sheehan, González, and George (1978).

In the case of the student background variables, the degree of between-class variation is a measure of nonrandom distribution of students among classes. Though we again find, as above, that the largest proportion of variation for most of these variables (all except **AGOCC**) is within classes, a substantial portion, of about the same magnitude as for the outcome variables, lies between classes.

---

[7] Klaus Galda has pointed out to us that some teachers may report similar attendance data for all students in a class because of the burden of keeping lengthy attendance records.

Several questions arise as to the sources of the variation of the outcome variables. Which of the student background variables help explain the within-class variation? How much of the between-class variation of the outcome variables can be explained by the student background variables and how much by the class background variables? We attempt to answer these and related questions in the remainder of this chapter.

4. THE TWO-STAGE ANALYSIS—THE MODELS

The basic idea behind our analysis is to express each of the outcome variables as a dependent variable in suitable linear models involving the background variables as independent variables. For example, one such model is of the form

$$(1) \qquad Y_{ij} = \mu + \sum_k \beta_k X_{ij}^{(k)} + \sum_l \gamma_l Z_i^{(l)} + \epsilon_{ij},$$

where

Y_{ij} is an outcome variable,

$X_{ij}^{(k)}$ are student background variables,

$Z_i^{(l)}$ are class background variables,

$i = 1, \ldots, I$, where I is the number of classes, and

$j = 1, \ldots, n_i$, where n_i is the number of students in the ith class.[8]

Our models differ from the one above mainly in that they do not treat the class-level variables simultaneously with student-level variables. With an eye towards disentangling the effects of these variables, we use a separate linear model for each. Proceeding in two stages, we first perform a student background regression and then a separate classroom background regression. We believe that the goals of accuracy of fit and clarity of interpretation are better met using what we will hereafter refer to as the two-stage analysis.

---

[8] Throughout the remainder of this chapter we use the generic notation Y for outcome variables, X for student background variables, and Z for classroom background variables.

The motivation behind this analysis is to disentangle the effects of the background variables from each other. To begin with, we partition each observation into its class mean and deviation from the class mean, that is, $Y_{ij} = Y_{i.} + Y'_{ij}$ where $Y_{i.} = \sum_j Y_{ij}/n_i$ and $Y'_{ij} = (Y_{ij} - Y_{i.})$, for outcome variables and similarly for background variables. We think of $Y_{i.}$ and Y'_{ij} as the between-class and within-class components, respectively, of Y_{ij}. We define within-class effects as effects of within-class components of background variables on the within-class components of outcome variables, and between-class effects as effects of between-class components of background variables on between-class components or means of outcome variables.[9] In stage I of our analysis we measure the within-class effects, and in stage II, the between-class effects. Because the class background variables are constant within classes, they yield no within-class effects. Hence, they are analyzed only in stage II.

The general form of our stage-I models is

$$(2) \qquad Y'_{ij} = \sum_k \beta_k X^{(k)'}_{ij} + \epsilon_{ij} .$$

These models are defined at the individual level and are linear models in the within-class components of outcome and student background variables.[10] The reader may recognize this model as a submodel in the more general analysis of covariance model

$$(3) \qquad Y_{ij} = \mu_i + \sum_k \beta_k X^{(k)}_{ij} + \epsilon_{ij} ,$$

which contains the variables in their original form but, instead of an overall constant term, contains a constant term μ_i for each class. The β coefficients in this model are precisely the same as in model (2).

Geometrically, the model (3) represents I parallel regression planes, corresponding to each of the I classes, with common slope ($\beta_1, \ldots, \beta_p$) and intercepts μ_i. The distance between the regression plane for class m

---

[9] We are making the assumption that class-level effects are exerted mainly through class means. There may be other, more complicated relationships, such as effects on the shapes of within-class distributions of the variables; such relationships are much more difficult to specify, and we do not consider them here.

[10] The natural constant term in model (2) is forced to be zero, because we have subtracted means out of every variable in the equation.

and that for class n is $|\mu_m - \mu_n|$.

We estimate the slopes of β_i and intercepts μ_i with ordinary least-squares methods and denote the estimates by $\hat{\beta}_i$ and $\hat{\mu}_i$ respectively.[11] The intercept estimates in model (3) may be expressed in the form

$$(4) \qquad \hat{\mu}_i = Y_{i.} - \sum_k \hat{\beta}_k X_{i.}^{(k)} ,$$

which makes it apparent that the $\hat{\mu}_i$ are just the class means of the outcome variable adjusted for the mean student-background characteristics. As part of our stage-I analysis, we provide graphical comparisons of the set of radio-class $\hat{\mu}_i$ with control-class $\hat{\mu}_i$ to shed some light on the unbiased effect of radio instruction.

The general form of our stage-II models is

$$(5) \qquad Y_{i.} = \mu + \sum_l \beta_l Z_i^{(l)} + \beta\,(\mathbf{BKGND}_i) + \epsilon_i .$$

These models are defined at the class level and are linear models in the means or between-class components of the outcome variables, the class background variables, and a new variable **BKGND**, which is the adjustment factor used to correct the class means in equation (4) above, that is,[12]

$$(6) \qquad \mathbf{BKGND}_i = Y_{i.} - \hat{\mu}_i = \sum_k \hat{\beta}_k X_{i.}^{(k)} .$$

Although the class background variables do not exert within-class effects, the student background variables may well exert between-class effects, especially in view of the nonrandom allocation of students to classes that we alluded to in the discussion of Table 4. The direction of these effects is well summarized by the variable **BKGND**, as we believe the student background effects should have the same direction between classes as they do within classes. We believe that direct estimation of the the between-class effects by putting the

---

[11] We place " $\hat{\ }$ " over a parameter to denote its estimate.

[12] The β coefficients in equation (6) refer to those in equation (4), not to those in model (5).

between-class components or means of the student background variables into model (5) is seriously biased by our inability to specify all of the nonstudent sources of between-class variation. For this reason, we elect to use **BKGND** as a proxy for student background effects. A further advantage of using **BKGND** is that we enlarge the context in which we evaluate the class-level effects while retaining the simplicity necessary for a clear analysis.

In the analysis of variance in the last section, we broke down the total variation of the outcome variables into the within-class variation and the between-class variation. The within-class variation results from the variation of the within-class component of the outcome variable, the dependent variable in model (2); the between-class variation (except for sample size factors) results from the variation of the between-class component of the outcome variable, the dependent variable in model (5). Thus, in the stage-I models we can assess the impact of the student background variables on the basis of their power to explain the within-class variation of the outcome variable, and in the stage-II models we can assess the impact of the class background variables on the basis of their power to explain the between-class variation. How we make these assessments is discussed in the next section.

We use a forward selection, stepwise inclusion, least-squares regression procedure for fitting all of our models, thereby including only those variables that explain a sizable portion of the variation on the step they enter (see Draper & Smith, 1966, p. 169). We do not force all the variables into the equation but instead let the data tell us which ones should be there. In effect, we derive smaller and simpler models, which are easier to understand. For instance, the interpretation of the regression coefficients as effects of the independent variables relies on the idea that these variables exert their effects while the other variables in the equation are controlled for, that is, held constant. In reality, the degree to which it is feasible to control for these other variables depends on the extent of intercorrelation. With fewer variables in the model, the correlation structure is not only more transparent but often less restrictive as well. Furthermore, with fewer sources of variation, there is less confounding of effects, thereby making evaluations clearer. We also avoid overfitting, a phenomenon which, by incorporating idiosyncracies of the data into the model, makes extrapolation of the results to similar populations suspect. These advantages of using a small set of independent variables are obtained with only slightly less power than would be obtained with a full model.

5. PRESENTATION OF THE TWO-STAGE ANALYSES

We present in this section in five tables the results of the two-stage analysis for each of the outcome variables. The formats of these tables are identical. We present first the fits of the stage-I model and then those of the stage-II model in all grades.

For each model we list the relevant portion of the variation of the outcome variable in the regression sample that the model aims to explain. For the stage-I models, this portion is the within-class variation, and in the stage-II models it is the between-class variation.[13]

As a measure of the magnitude of the joint effect of the independent variables in our models, we present in the column labeled *EXPL* the values of R^2 for each of our regression models. This R^2 is the proportion of reduction of within-class variation in stage-I models or reduction of between-class variation in stage-II models obtained by using the regression line as a mean.

Next, we list in the order of entry the independent variables included in the particular regression. This order was determined by the forward-selection, stepwise-regression procedure, where at each step, the independent variable with the largest partial correlation (in absolute value) with the outcome variable among those variables not yet in the equation is entered. No more variables are entered when the largest remaining partial correlation is not significantly different from zero.[14]

The square of the partial correlation is just the proportion of the remaining variation that an independent variable would explain if it entered the regression on that step. Thus, our stepwise procedure selects variables on the basis of their explanatory power at that step. Unfortunately, this explanatory power depends very much on the order of entry when intercorrelations among the variables are present. However, how variables exert their predictive power in the final model does not depend on the order of entry. Therefore, we have elected to present two other measures of the explanatory power of each of the independent variables. The first measure, which we denote as *initial power*, is simply the proportion of the total variation that

---

[13] We again remind the reader that because of the missing-value structure, we are forced to use smaller data sets for fitting the linear models, so that our estimates of between-class variation in Tables 5 through 9 (presented later in this section) are apt to differ somewhat from the values for R^2 presented in Table 4.

[14] We set the significance level at .05 here.

the variable explains by itself, that is, R^2 if it entered the regression model first. It is the square of the simple Pearson correlation coefficient of the variable **RADIO** with the class means of the outcome variable. This measure of power is clear and simple, but it fails to take into account the potential confounding effect of the other variables. The second measure, which we denote as *adjusted power*, is the proportion of the total variation, or R^2, that the variable would explain if it had entered the regression equation last, after all the other variables in the model were forced in. This quantity is also sometimes known as the square of the part correlation. This measure takes into account the potential effect of the other variables but does not tell us how the interrelations of the effects act to exert their power. However, the disparity between these two measures can provide some insight into how nonuniquely the variable exerts its effect in the full model.

For each independent variable in the full model we present the least squares estimate of the partial regression coefficient ($\hat{\beta}$), together with the standard error of the estimate (*STD ERR* $\hat{\beta}$) and the partial F statistic for testing the hypothesis that the partial regression coefficient in the whole model is zero. We regard the F statistic as a general measure of relative importance and significance of fit of the β coefficient in the model, rather than treat it in the strict probabilistic sense. We should also point out that sizable F values will not necessarily imply strong explanatory power, as can be seen from the other statistics in the tables.

We also present in this section, for each outcome variable across all grades, the graphical plots of the class means adjusted for the background variables—the least squares estimates $\hat{\mu}_i$ defined in equation (4). We plot the values corresponding to radio and control classes separately to see the potential effects of radio lessons on the distribution of adjusted class means. The reader will notice that we have placed asterisks next to some of the points in the plots. These points correspond to at least one intercept estimate based on less than five observations due to the missing-value structure. Because these values are such imprecise estimates, we dropped them from further analysis in Stage II. Though we do present these estimates in our plots, the reader is advised to be skeptical of these values.

Standardized Posttest and Pretest Results

Because we are interested in grade-to-grade comparisons of our results, we have replaced the variables **POST** and **PRE** by their standardized scores **SPOST** and **SPRE**.[15] In this way the scales along

---

[15] A standardized score Y_{ij}^* of Y_{ij} is obtained as $Y_{ij}^* = (Y_{ij} - Y_{..})/S$ where $Y_{..}$ is the overall mean and S is the standard deviation.

which these variables are measured will have a generalizable meaning. All of our other variables are measured by the same scale over grades, making further standardization unnecessary. Notice that this standardization affects only $\hat{\beta}$ and $STD\ ERR\ \hat{\beta}$ in the regressions. The variance-explanatory measures are unchanged.

Posttest

Table 5 presents the results of the two-stage analysis of the standardized posttest score (**SPOST**). In stage I, **SPRE** exhibits by far the most explanatory power of the student background variables across all three grades. By itself, it explains about 30% of the within-class variation of **SPOST** in Grades 1 and 3 and more than 43% in Grade 2. Of the other student background variables, only **AGE** in Grade 1 had enough additional predictive power after **SPRE** to enter the model. By itself, **AGE** explains 6% of the within-class variation of **SPOST**, although after adjustment for **SPRE** it explains only 1%. Similarly, after adjustment for **AGE**, the explanatory power of **SPRE** is reduced from 28.2% to 23.2%, although both of these adjustments (which are

TABLE 5

Two-stage Analysis of **SPOST**

Grade	Variation[a]	EXPL	Variable	Initial power	Adjusted power	$\hat{\beta}$	STD ERR $\hat{\beta}$	F
				Stage I				
1	.607	.292	**SPRE**	.282	.232	.446	.0333	180.00
			AGE	.060	.010	.060	.0213	7.88
2	.727	.433	**SPRE**	.433	.433	.645	.0309	435.01
3	.703	.304	**SPRE**	.304	.304	.524	.0413	165.67
				Stage II				
1	.393	.720	**RADIO**	.594	.525	.941	.1037	82.40
			BKGND	.182	.097	.065	.0165	15.28
			RURAL	.014	.027	−.207	.1019	4.14
2	.273	.749	**BKGND**	.727	.339	.110	.0179	37.84
			RADIO	.410	.022	.205	.1306	2.46
3	.297	.846	**RADIO**	.446	.468	.814	.1043	60.92
			BKGND	.376	.368	.141	.0203	47.88
			CLSIZ	.001	.055	.011	.0042	7.17

[a] The variation for Stage I is the within-class variation; for Stage II, the between-class variation.

consistent with our observation of a simple correlation between **SPRE** and **AGE** in Grade 1 of .303) do not affect the dominance of **SPRE**. It is interesting that even with the addition of **AGE** to the stage-I model, less of the within-class variation is explained in Grade 1 than with just **SPRE** in the higher grades (.292 versus .433 and .304). This suggests that the within-class variation of posttest scores is less predictable or more unstable in Grade 1.

The coefficient estimates $\hat{\beta}$ for **SPRE**, which are precise in all grades according to the relatively small standard errors, suggest that we can expect changes of .446, .645, and .524 standard deviations in posttest score in Grades 1, 2, and 3, respectively, with a change of one standard deviation in pretest score. (In Grade 1, we must control for **AGE**.) The variable **AGE** in Grade 1, when controlling for **SPRE**, predicts a .06 change in **SPOST** with each increasing year of age, though this coefficient is not as significant.

The plots of the stage-I **SPOST** adjusted class means in Figure 1 point up some clear differences between radio and control classes. In Grade 1, we see that radio classes score almost uniformly higher on the posttest. In later grades, the effect of radio is not so sharp. In Grade 2, there are five control classes scoring as high as the radio classes, one, in fact, scoring higher than all classes. And in Grade 3, although radio classes appear to score higher, the two groups overlap quite a bit. However, in all three grades, if we ignore the most extreme and the poorly estimated (*) classes, the radio scores are uniformly higher. This is important, since we expect that classes that are not at the extremes make up the bulk of the population.

Consistent with these observations, the stage-II analysis indicated that the variables **RADIO** and **BKGND** share the strongest predictive power of **SPOST** across all grades. The effect of **RADIO** was visible in Figure 1; the effect of **BKGND** is mainly the strong **SPRE** effect manifesting itself in the between-class variation. In all three cases, **RADIO** by itself explains a very large proportion of the class-level variation of posttest score, 59.4% in Grade 1, 41% in Grade 2, and 44.6% in Grade 3. These percentages are extraordinarily large in view of the intraclass correlations for **POST** in Table 4. It was pointed out earlier that only about half of the **POST** between-class variation could be attributed to class-level effects.

The effect of the variable **BKGND**, by itself, is less than that of **RADIO** in Grades 1 and 3, where it explains 18.2% and 37.6%, respectively, of the variance. But in Grade 2, it explains an overwhelming 72.7% by itself. However, the explanatory powers of **RADIO** and **BKGND** are severely decreased in the model for Grade 2 after adjustment for each other, due to a high correlation (.613)—an unfortunate randomization outcome in the sample. Because of the results

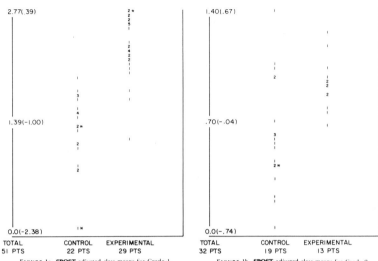

FIGURE 1a. **SPOST** adjusted class means for Grade 1.

FIGURE 1b. **SPOST** adjusted class means for Grade 2.

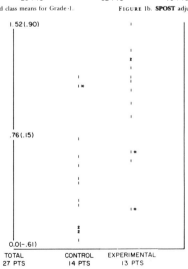

FIGURE 1c. **SPOST** adjusted class means for Grade 3.

in the other grades, it seems reasonable to believe that the effect of **RADIO** alone in Grade 2 is not spurious, that is, due to a confounded **BKGND** effect, but rather that the increased power of **BKGND** is due to an added **RADIO** effect.

In addition to **BKGND** and **RADIO**, the variables **RURAL** in Grade 1 and **CLSIZ** in Grade 3 entered the class-level regression models on the last step to explain additional variations of 2.7% and 5.5%, respectively. Though their power is substantially smaller than that of **BKGND** or **RADIO**, it is interesting to note that they both gain importance after adjustment in the models for the other variables. Thus, their effects rely on controlling for **RADIO** and **BKGND**.

According to our β estimates, controlling for the other variables in the models, we expect in radio classes increases of .914, .110, and .814 in the standard deviations of posttest scores in Grades 1, 2, and 3, respectively. These coefficient estimates are very significant in Grades 1 and 3, but not in Grade 2. Because of the the large correlation between **RADIO** and **BKGND** in Grade 2, the effective increase in posttest score due to radio is probably much larger. Again controlling for the other variables, rural classes tend to decrease the posttest score by .207 standard deviation in Grade 1, and increasing class size tends to increase posttest score at the rate of .011 standard deviation per additional student in Grade 3. Due to a strong negative correlation between **CLSIZ** and **RURAL** in Grade 3 ($-.637$), this class size effect may be partially a rural effect.

Attendance

Table 6 presents the results of the two-stage analysis of average student attendance in days per months attended (**ATTAV**). Perhaps what is most striking in the stage-I analysis is the relative ineffectiveness of the student background variables to explain the within-class variation. As was pointed out in the discussion of Table 4, the proportion of within-class variation of **ATTAV** is very much smaller than that of any of the other background variables. (It is even smaller in Grades 1 and 3 of the regression sample.) That this might have been caused by artificial means, like the teacher's data-collection habits, could well account for the low variance-explanatory power of the student variables.

Although their predictive power is weak, the effects of the student background variables are consistent. The variable **SPRE** enters the models on the second step in all three grades, **DIST** appears in Grades 1 and 2, and **AGE** appears in Grades 2 and 3. The variables **MALE** and **NRPT** appear only once—**MALE** in Grade 2 and **NRPT** in Grade 3. Except for **AGE** and **NRPT** in Grade 3, which by them-

TABLE 6

Two-stage Analysis of **ATTAV**

Grade	Vari-ation[a]	EXPL	Variable	Initial power	Adjusted power	$\hat{\beta}$	STD ERR $\hat{\beta}$	F
				Stage I				
1	.387	.013	DIST	.008	.008	−.127	.0550	5.34
			SPRE	.005	.005	.114	.0606	3.57
2	.478	.272	MALE	.008	.012	−.272	.0991	7.55
			SPRE	.005	.009	.133	.0540	6.03
			AGE	.005	.009	−.072	.0308	5.54
			DIST	.003	.004	.065	.0377	3.00
3	.371	.057	AGE	.040	.030	−.103	.0281	13.52
			SPRE	.008	.008	.100	.0529	3.63
			NRPT	.021	.008	−.165	.0895	3.39
				Stage II				
1	.613	.485	RURAL	.312	.242	−1.795	.4710	14.52
			RADIO	.070	.076	.999	.4684	4.55
			BKGND	.117	.084	8.245	3.6763	5.03
			TED	.012	.045	.193	.1184	2.65
2	.522	.414	RURAL	.302	.365	−1.301	.3366	14.93
			RADIO	.048	.012	−.733	.3423	4.58
3	.629	.118	RADIO	.118	.118	−.893	.5079	3.09

[a] The variation for Stage I is the within-class variation; for Stage II, the between-class variation.

selves explain 4% and 2.1% of the within-class variation of **ATTAV**, no other variable accounts on its own for more than 1%. In Grade 1, the explanatory power of the variables remains the same when they are entered on the last step, suggesting that **SPRE** and **DIST** exert relatively independent effects. In Grade 2, the explanatory power of every variable increases when entered on the last step, suggesting that the variables are exerting compensatory effects. This is consistent with the following significant[16] sample correlations among the student variables in Grade 2—**SPRE** with **MALE** at .108, **SPRE** with **AGE** at .222, and **AGE** with **DIST** at .110. In the

---

[16] We again use statistical significance, here at the .01 level under the standard normality assumptions, as an index of importance.

model for Grade 3, the correlation between **AGE** and **NRPT** is .174, suggesting that these may act as proxies for one another in exerting their effects. This claim is supported by the fact that the explanatory power for each decreases when it enters the model last.

The **SPRE** regression coefficient estimates suggest an increase of between .1 and .133 in average attendance with an increase of one standard deviation in pretest score. Increasing distance from school predicts lower average attendance in Grade 1 but (counterintuitively) higher average attendance in Grade 2. We are somewhat skeptical of the result for Grade 2 because the three other student variables in the equation can influence the effect through correlation. The **AGE** coefficient estimates indicate that increasing age decreases average attendance. We are more confident of the effect in Grade 3 because $\hat\beta$ is more significant and there are fewer variables in the regression. Finally, males in Grade 2 and students with a greater history of repetition in Grade 3 have lower attendance averages. We remind the reader that the interpretations given above of the regression coefficients require that we control for the other variables in the equation, that is, that we vary one independent variable while holding all the others constant. As the intercorrelations and dependencies of the effects in the model increase, this interpretation becomes less realistic. In Grade 1, however, our interpretation seems safe. In the other grades, especially Grade 2, we must be very cautious.

Figure 2, the plots of the adjusted means, indicates that radio classes have generally higher attendance rates only in Grade 1. Indeed, in Grade 1, the radio attendance averages are more consistent (the data points are less spread out) and tend to be larger. In Grade 2, the radio classes fall into two groups, one with attendance rates in the neighborhood of the average control-class attendance rate and one somewhat lower. In Grade 3, although the lowest and highest attendance rates are displayed by control and radio classes, respectively, the general trend is apparently towards lower attendance rates in radio classes. It is interesting to note that attendance rates seem to have a much broader range in Grade 1 than in Grades 2 or 3, as is indicated by the different scales.

The stage-II analysis bears out quite clearly the direction of the effects of radio on class attendance averages that were observed in Figure 2. However, the variable **RADIO** is not as powerful here as it was in explaining posttest variation. Indeed, by itself, **RADIO** explains 7%, 4.8%, and 11.8% of the within-class variation in Grades 1, 2, and 3, respectively. Its final effect increases slightly with the introduction of other variables in the model for Grade 1, although it decreases markedly in the model for Grade 2 with the introduction of

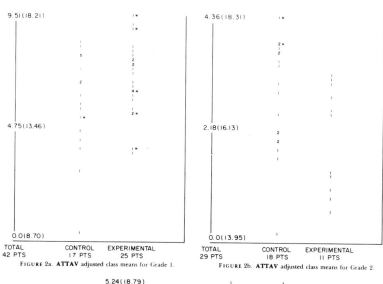

9.51(18.21)

4.75(13.46)

0.0(8.70)

TOTAL   CONTROL   EXPERIMENTAL
42 PTS   17 PTS   25 PTS

FIGURE 2a. **ATTAV** adjusted class means for Grade 1.

4.36(18.31)

2.18(16.13)

0.0(13.95)

TOTAL   CONTROL   EXPERIMENTAL
29 PTS   18 PTS   11 PTS

FIGURE 2b. **ATTAV** adjusted class means for Grade 2.

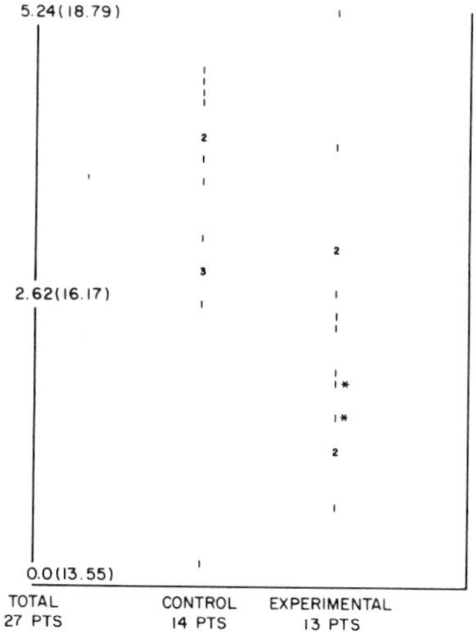

5.24(18.79)

2.62(16.17)

0.0(13.55)

TOTAL   CONTROL   EXPERIMENTAL
27 PTS   14 PTS   13 PTS

FIGURE 2c. **ATTAV** adjusted class means for Grade 3.

RURAL. The regression coefficient estimates suggest a difference of .999, −.733, and −.893 in average days attended per month between radio and control classes when the other variables can be effectively controlled for.

The variable **RURAL** has a much larger effect on **ATTAV** than does **RADIO** in Grades 1 and 2, where **RURAL** enters the models first to explain more than 30% of the class-level variance in both cases. Even when it enters the model last, its explanatory power is much greater than that of the other variables. The coefficient estimates are very significant and indicate that class attendance rates in rural classes are, on the average, smaller by 1.795 and 1.301 days in Grades 1 and 2, respectively—again, controlling for the other factors.

In the model for Grade 1, we notice that the variable **BKGND**, in this case a linear combination of class averages of **DIST** and **SPRE**, is more powerful than **RADIO**, explaining 11.7% of the class-level variation by itself and 8.4% after adjusting for all the other variables. We note that although **BKGND** is correlated with **ATTAV** at −.258 in Grade 3, its absence in the model is probably due to a correlation with **RADIO** of .319. The danger of this omission is twofold. Not only do we miss the potential effect of **BKGND**, but we also become uncertain about the observed effect of **RADIO**, in that it may well be acting as a proxy for other effects.

Finally, **TED** (the teacher's education) also enters the model for Grade 1 to explain 4.5% of the variation when it enters. This is substantially more than the 1.2% it would explain by itself, so we cannot be sure what part of its effect is really due to the education of the teacher.

Failure

Table 7 presents the results of the two-stage analysis of the indicator variable of whether or not a student failed the final exams (**FAIL**). In contrast to **ATTAV**, the bulk of the variation of **FAIL** lies within classes, suggesting stable failure rates across classes. A decision mechanism consistent with this observation would be for the teacher simply to rank the students in each class and then fail a fixed percentage rather than try to base the failure decision on some absolute criteria (see chap. 6). Looked at in this way, the stage-I models predict how the students are ranked within classes.

Of all our student-level variables, pretest score is the most powerful predictor of failure. In all grade models, its variance-explanatory power dominates that of the other variables both before and after adjustment for other variables. By itself, it seems to exert its strongest effect in the first grade, where it explains 12% of the within-class

TABLE 7

Two-stage Analysis of **FAIL**

Grade	Variation[a]	EXPL	Variable	Initial power	Adjusted power	$\hat{\beta}$	STD ERR $\hat{\beta}$	F
				Stage I				
1	.883	.132	**SPRE**	.120	.098	−.156	.0158	97.54
			MALE	.001	.007	.076	.0287	6.99
			AGE	.034	.005	−.022	.0101	4.82
2	.888	.066	**SPRE**	.044	.049	−.097	.0174	31.22
			AGOCC	.010	.014	−.153	.0522	8.61
			MALE	.001	.007	.067	.0328	4.21
			DIST	.005	.005	−.012	.0076	2.63
3	.840	.098	**SPRE**	.068	.071	−.094	.0162	33.36
			AGE	.023	.024	.028	.0085	11.24
			DIST	.007	.004	.022	.0153	2.12
				Stage II				
1	.117	.213	**BKGND**	.125	.146	.926	.3136	8.72
			RURAL	.067	.088	.098	.0426	5.24
2	.112	.148	**RURAL**	.148	.148	−.097	.0467	4.35
3	.160	.142	**RADIO**	.142	.142	.076	.0383	3.96

[a] The variation for Stage I is the within-class variation; for Stage II, the between-class variation.

variation. In Grades 2 and 3 it explains 4.4% and 6.8%, respectively. These levels of explanatory power are not altered very much after the entry of other variables, so that we may attribute the effect essentially to pretest score. In all cases, very significant negative β estimates indicate that lower pretest scores predict a higher tendency to fail, as we would expect.[17]

---

[17] We have used a linear model to predict failure. Unfortunately, our predicted values for this model will not be 0,1 variables. We interpret the predicted values here as measures of tendency to fail. In this context, only the sign of the regression coefficients is clearly meaningful. An alternative model for the stage-I results would be a logistic model, which for this situation is highly interpretable. Unfortunately, the overall variance-decomposition interpretations are then not clear. The linear model, we believe, is an adequate approximation to the logistic model in our samples, where the fits are not very precise. In this way, we can use the logistic interpretation of predicting tendency to fail and still adhere to our fundamental variance-decomposition techniques. These same comments hold true for the **DROP** and **RENRL** stage-I analyses presented below.

In terms of power, **AGE** is the next most important predictor of failure, appearing in the models for Grades 1 and 3. By itself, it explains 3.7% and 2.3% of the variation in Grades 1 and 3, respectively. In Grade 1, a negative β estimate suggests that younger children are more likely to fail, whereas in Grade 3 the direction is reversed—increasing age predicts a higher tendency to fail. In Grade 3, the explanatory power of **AGE** is relatively stable, but in Grade 1, where it is correlated with pretest score at .326, its adjusted power diminishes.

Lesser effects are also exerted by the variable **MALE** in Grades 1 and 2, by **DIST** in Grades 2 and 3, and by **AGOCC** in Grade 2. The small and increasing power of the variable **MALE** after adjustment suggests that its effect is compensatory and probably unimportant. The effect of **DIST** is more stable, yet poorly estimated β coefficients add uncertainty even to the direction of its effects, especially in light of the reversal in the sign of β from Grade 2 to Grade 3. The power of **AGOCC** is not only stable but also a little larger than these, between 1% and 1.4%. β is significant and indicates that in Grade 2 students from an agricultural family are less likely to fail.

Turning to the plots of the adjusted means in Figure 3, the only clear location-shift effect is in Grade 2, where the radio group of classes appears to have higher adjusted failure rates. However, even here we should note that it is two or three radio classes with high failure rates that suggest the shift. In Grade 1, the radio group seems only to be less spread out; most of the classes with extreme failure rates belong to the control group. In Grade 3, the trend seems to favor control classes with slightly lower failure rates.

In the stage-II models, we find **RADIO** only in the model for Grade 3, where it is alone and explains 14.2% of the class-level variation of **FAIL**. β indicates that we expect 7.6% more failures in radio classes. In Grade 2, we find that **RURAL** alone overwhelms the power of any other variable by explaining 14.8% of the variation. Its estimated effect suggests that rural classes have 9.7% fewer failures. In the model for Grade 1 we find **BKGND** and **RURAL** explaining 12.5% and 6.7% of the variation by themselves, and both increasing slightly in power after adjustment for each other. Here, the **BKGND** β suggests that the classes in the sample that have higher pretest scores and older children have lower failure rates. Interestingly, the **RURAL** β suggests higher failure rates in rural classes, a reversal from Grade 2. Although **BKGND** and **RURAL** are each weaker in Grade 1 than is **RURAL** in Grade 2 or **RADIO** in Grade 3, they are jointly more powerful in explaining the class-level variation of **FAIL**.

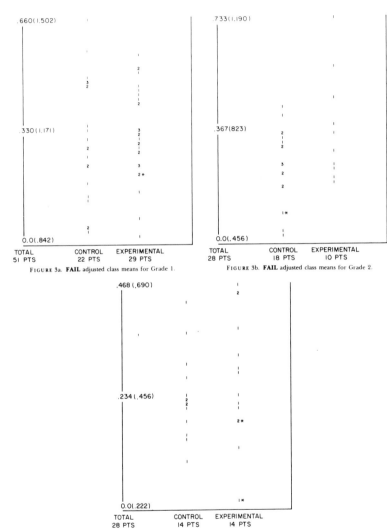

FIGURE 3a. **FAIL** adjusted class means for Grade 1.

FIGURE 3b. **FAIL** adjusted class means for Grade 2.

FIGURE 3c. **FAIL** adjusted class means for Grade 3.

It is important to consider that the overall power of these class variables is somewhat diminished by the low percentages of between-class variation in **FAIL**, which ranges from 11% to 16%.

Dropout

Table 8 presents the results of the two-stage analysis of the indicator variable of whether or not a student dropped out during the school year (**DROP**). As with the variable **FAIL**, the bulk of the variation of **DROP** lies within classes. However, a teacher-controlled mechanism here cannot control the real dropout rate, since during the year dropout is not a teacher-made decision. An examination of the class-level data revealed that a dropout rate of zero was reported in 39%, 55%, and 70% of the classes in Grades 1, 2, and 3, respectively. Intuitively, these percentages seem surprisingly large, giving rise to the suspicion that the teachers did not accurately record the attendance data from which dropout rates were constructed. However, because teachers are bound by law to record accurate registry figures, we have kept these classes in our analysis. Unfortunately, this

TABLE 8

Two-stage Analysis of **DROP**

Grade	Vari- ation[a]	EXPL	Variable	Initial power	Adjusted power	$\hat{\beta}$	STD ERR $\hat{\beta}$	F
				Stage I				
1	.803	.011	**NRPT**	.008	.008	−.046	.0118	15.31
			MALE	.003	.003	.034	.0151	4.96
2	.906	.000						
3	.864	.044	**AGE**	.044	.044	.025	.0041	36.90
				Stage II				
1	.197	.234	**RURAL**	.139	.201	.147	.0432	11.55
			CLSIZ	.018	.069	.004	.0019	3.98
			TEXP	.011	.040	.003	.0022	2.32
2	.094	.000						
3	.136	.000						

Note. No linear model was found to fit the data reasonably in Grade 2 of Stage I and in Grades 2 and 3 of Stage II. In these cases we report .000 for EXPL and nothing else.

[a] The variation for Stage I is the within-class variation; for Stage II, the between-class variation.

unusual distribution of dropouts makes it difficult to detect effects with our linear models. Finally, except in Grade 1, far more of the classes with a dropout rate of zero were control classes, introducing the possibility of bias against radio.

The stage-I models are weak, although large within-class variation somewhat inflates their effect. The model for Grade 1 explained 1.1%, and for Grade 3, 4.4%. Of the variables in Grade 2, we could not find any linear model with a reasonable fit.

In Grade 1, the variables **NRPT** and **MALE** entered the model to explain .8% and .3%, respectively, of the within-class variation both before and after adjustment. The stability of their power and the significance of the coefficient estimates lead us to trust their effects, despite their weak power. Interestingly, students in Grade 1 with higher repetition rates tend to drop out less, supporting the hypothesis that many students expect to repeat before they advance (see Searle et al., 1978). Male students in Grade 1 appear to have higher dropout rates. In Grade 3, **AGE** is the only variable in the model. It explains 4.4% of the within-class variation—more than any other student variable in any grade. A very significant $\hat{\beta}$ indicates that increasing age predicts a higher tendency to drop out.

Because of the weak power of the stage-I models, the plots of the adjusted means in Figure 4 are very close to the plots of the unadjusted class means in Grades 1 and 3 and are just the class means in Grade 2. Across all grades, it appears that of the classes with high dropout rates, most were radio classes. The clustering appearances in Grades 1 and 3 are probably due to the unusual distribution of the class averages.

As was the stage-I analysis, the stage-II analysis was plagued by the weak explanatory power of the models. In fact, only in Grade 1 were we able to find a linear model that could be fitted with reasonable precision. The model for Grade 1 does explain a reasonable 23.4% of the variation, although this amount is somewhat diminished in overall importance because of the low percentage, 19.7%, of between-class variation. The variables **RURAL, CLSIZ,** and **TEXP** all entered the model for Grade 1, with **RURAL** by far the most powerful. All variables increased in power after adjustment, suggesting that their effects depend on controlling for each other. The coefficient estimates, of which only that for **RURAL** is very significant, suggest that rural classes, larger classes, and classes with more experienced teachers have higher dropout rates. We should remark that the variables most highly correlated with **DROP** in the other grades were **TED** in Grade 2 at .247 and **CLSIZ** in Grade 3 at .221. Although we do not present them in linear models, the respective explanatory powers of **TED** and **CLSIZ** in those grades are estimated at .061 and .049.

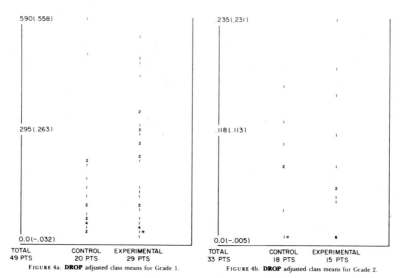

FIGURE 4a. **DROP** adjusted class means for Grade 1.

FIGURE 4b. **DROP** adjusted class means for Grade 2.

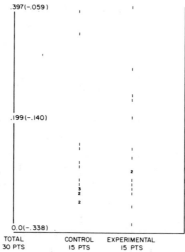

FIGURE 4c. **DROP** adjusted class means for Grade 3.

Reenrollment

Table 9 presents the results of the two-stage analysis of the indicator variable of whether or not a student reenrolled in the following school year (**RENRL**). The reenrollment data suffer from the same bimodality effect as the dropout data do. Inspection of the class means revealed that 54%, 60%, and 32% of the classes in Grades 1, 2, and 3 reported perfect reenrollments. The possibility of negligent collection of data seems large here in view of the difficulties surrounding keeping track of the students after the school year. Unfortunately, there appeared to be no unbiased way of removing any of these perfect reenrollment classes.

Although the stage-I models are uniformly weak, the consistent entry of **AGE** as the most powerful explanatory variable is revealing. It gains power as we go from Grade 1 to Grade 3, correspondingly explaining 1%, 3.8%, and 4.1% of the within-class variance by itself. The coefficient estimates indicate that increasing age predicts a lower tendency to reenroll, and that this effect is more pronounced in Grades 2 and 3. The variable **SPRE** enters the model for Grade 2 as well, suggesting that higher pretest scores predict reenrollment. It is interesting to note that both **AGE** and **SPRE** gain predictive power

TABLE 9

Two-stage Analysis of **RENRL**

Grade	Vari-ation[a]	EXPL	Variable	Initial power	Adjusted power	$\hat{\beta}$	STD ERR $\hat{\beta}$	F
				Stage I				
1	.701	.010	**AGE**	.010	.010	−.015	.0040	13.84
2	.714	.046	**AGE**	.038	.043	−.035	.0070	24.60
			SPRE	.003	.008	.026	.0123	4.54
3	.842	.041	**AGE**	.041	.041	−.036	.0071	25.15
				Stage II				
1	.299	.092	**USH**	.092	.092	.094	.0436	4.64
2	.286	.220	**BKGND**	.220	.220	2.165	.7995	7.33
3	.158	.373	**BKGND**	.179	.221	1.961	.7208	7.40
			RADIO	.152	.194	−.140	.0548	6.52

[a] The variation for Stage I is the within-class variation; for Stage II, the between-class variation.

after adjusting for each other, presumably correcting for those older students with higher pretest scores.

The most revealing quality of the plots of the adjusted means in Figure 5 is the consistent presence of classes with very low reenrollment rates. Only in Grade 3 do the radio classes appear to have a tendency towards lower reenrollment rates. However, we should add here that all of the classes in Grade 3 reporting perfect reenrollment were in the control group.

In the stage-II analysis, we note the appearance of **BKGND** in the models for Grades 2 and 3. It has the largest class-level explanatory power, indicating that in these grades the student background characteristics, notably age, play an important part in explaining the between-class variation. The effect of **BKGND** is positive in both cases, suggesting that the direction is consistent with the effect found in the stage-I analysis. The variable **USH** makes its first appearance in the **RENRL** model for Grade 1 as the only variable with reasonable class-level explanatory power. Its effect seems to be that urban classes with shifts have higher reenrollment rates. This finding is consistent with the hypothesis that urban shift classes exist where there is a high demand for schooling. Finally, **RADIO** makes its only appearance in the model for Grade 3, explaining 15.5% of the variation by itself and then increasing in power after adjustment for **BKGND**. Its estimated effect is negative—that is, radio classes tend to have lower reenrollment rates—although this observation is somewhat mitigated by the peculiar data distributions mentioned in connection with the intercept plots above.

6. CONCLUSIONS

Important Explanatory Variables

Table 10 summarizes the background variables that entered the particular models considered in the two-stage analysis. An asterisk indicates those cases in which a variable entered a model. We now examine each background variable to see where it effectively predicted outcome variables. Although some variables with reasonable power are bound to be left out here simply because of their correlations with other variables, we believe that this pattern is not widespread and does not systematically eliminate any one variable. In the case of **RADIO** this is borne out, as we see in the followng subsection.

The most consistent predictors of within-class variation were **PRE** and **AGE**. The variable **PRE** was a very powerful predictor of **POST** and **FAIL**, which are outcome variables measuring student performance. It was somewhat important in **ATTAV** and, for Grade 2 of

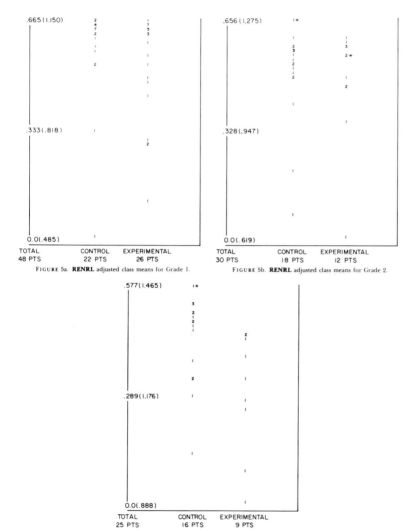

.665 (1.150)

.333(.818)

0.0(.485)

TOTAL   CONTROL   EXPERIMENTAL
48 PTS   22 PTS   26 PTS

FIGURE 5a. **RENRL** adjusted class means for Grade 1.

.656 (1.275)

.328(.947)

0.0(.619)

TOTAL   CONTROL   EXPERIMENTAL
30 PTS   18 PTS   12 PTS

FIGURE 5b. **RENRL** adjusted class means for Grade 2.

.577(1.465)

.289(1.176)

0.0(.888)

TOTAL   CONTROL   EXPERIMENTAL
25 PTS   16 PTS   9 PTS

FIGURE 5c. **RENRL** adjusted class means for Grade 3.

TABLE 10

The Models[a] in Which Background Variables Appeared

Variable	Total	POST			ATTAV			FAIL			DROP			RENRL		
		1	2	3	1	2	3	1	2	3	1	2	3	1	2	3
Student background variables																
PRE	10	*	*	*	*	*	*	*	*	*					*	
MALE	4					*		*	*		*					
AGE	9	*			*	*	*		*		*			*	*	*
AGOCC	1								*							
DIST	4				*	*			*	*						
NRPT	2					*					*					
Classroom background variables																
RURAL	6	*			*	*			*	*	*					
USH	1											*				
UNOSH	0															
RADIO	8	*	*	*	*	*	*		*							*
CLSIZ	2	*									*					
TAGE	0															
TED	1				*											
TEXP	1										*					
BKGND	7	*	*	*	*				*						*	*

[a] The models are for Grades 1, 2, and 3.

RENRL, in outcome variables measuring demand for schooling. Thus, students with higher pretest scores have higher posttest scores, are less likely to fail, have slightly better attendance, and, in Grade 2, are slightly more prone to reenroll.

The variable **AGE** found its way into at least one grade-model for every outcome variable. We observed that older students have higher posttest scores in Grade 1 and lower attendance in Grades 2 and 3, are less likely to fail in Grade 1 but more likely to fail in Grade 3, are more likely to drop out in Grade 3, and are less likely to reenroll in all grades. The explanatory power was about the same in all the models **AGE** entered.

The less consistent background variables—**MALE**, **DIST**, **NRPT**, and **AGOCC**—found their way only into regression models for **ATTAV**, **FAIL**, and Grade 1 of **DROP**. The general directions of their effects are as follows: Boys have lower attendance in Grade 2, are more likely to fail in Grades 1 and 2, and are more likely to drop out in Grade 1; students who live farther away attend fewer days in Grade 1 but more in Grade 2 and are less likely to fail in Grade 2 but more likely in Grade 3; students with higher repetition rates have lower attendance in Grade 3 and are less likely to drop out in Grade 1; and, finally, students from agricultural families are less likely to fail in Grade 2.

By far the most consistent class-level explanatory variables were **RADIO**, **BKGND**, and **RURAL**—in that order. As we describe in more detail below, **RADIO** had a small effect only in Grades 1 and 2 on **FAIL** and **RENRL** and in all grades on **DROP**. The the variable that measured the effect of the nonrandom allocation of students to classes on class-level variation, **BKGND**, found its way into all **POST** regressions, Grade 1 of **ATTAV** and **FAIL**, and Grades 2 and 3 of **RENRL**. In those cases, its direction was positive, implying that the within-class effects of the stage-I models were exerting similar effects at the class level.

RURAL exerted its effect most consistently in Grade 1, entering all models there but **RENRL**. In Grade 2, it continued to be important in **ATTAV** and **FAIL**, and then ceased to have any effect in Grade 3. In general, we found that rural classes had lower posttest scores in Grade 1, lower attendance rates in Grades 1 and 2, higher failure rates in Grade 1 but lower rates in Grade 2, and higher dropout rates in Grade 1.

The observed effects of the other class-level variables were as follows: Larger classes had slightly higher posttest scores in Grade 3 and slightly higher dropout rates in Grade 1, teachers with more education had slightly higher attendance in their classes in Grade 1, teachers with more experience had slightly higher dropout rates in Grade 1, and urban shift schools had higher reenrollment in Grade 1. The variables **UNOSH** and **TAGE** entered none of the models.

The Explanatory Power of Radio

As we have have seen, **RADIO** does not appear in some of the stage-II models. Furthermore, even in those models in which it does appear, we often suspect that **RADIO** is acting as a proxy for variables not in the model. Therefore, in Table 11, we have presented the *initial* and *adjusted power* measures of **RADIO** for every outcome variable in every grade. The *adjusted power* estimate here is based on a full model; that is, it is the proportion of within-class variation that **RADIO** explains after adjusting for all the class-level variables we have defined, including **BKGND**. We also include a third measure that we denote as *% adjusted power*, which is the proportion of remaining within-class variation that **RADIO** explains after adjusting for all the class-level variables. It is just the square of the partial correlation. This measure scales the second measure up, so that it has a range between 0 and 1. In a way, this is a more judicious measure; otherwise, different powerful variables can force the effect of **RADIO** to be small regardless of correlation.

The strongest potential effect by far of **RADIO** was in explaining **POST** variation. As was pointed out in the **POST** analysis, the low adjusted power in Grade 2 is probably due to an unfortunate correlation with **BKGND**. The next most powerful influence of **RADIO** was

TABLE 11

The Explanatory Power of **RADIO**

Variable	Grade	Initial power	Adjusted power	% adjusted power
POST	1	.594	.252	.509
	2	.410	.009	.038
	3	.446	.422	.744
ATTAV	1	.070	.054	.101
	2	(−).049	(−).072	.120
	3	(−).118	(−).038	.050
FAIL	1	.003	(−).004	.006
	2	.040	.005	.007
	3	.142	.127	.159
DROP	1	.046	.002	.003
	2	.052	.120	.018
	3	.010	.020	.031
RENRL	1	(−).005	(−).015	.018
	2	(−).000	.001	.001
	3	(−).152	(−).162	.256

Note. The symbol (−) is placed in front of the powers in those situations where the direction of the effect was negative.

observed in **ATTAV**, **FAIL**, and **RENRL** only in Grade 3, where the effect was reasonably stable before and after adjustment. **RADIO** exerted modest effects on **ATTAV** and **DROP** in Grades 1 and 2 and on **FAIL** in Grade 2. Of these cases, only in **ATTAV** did the power of **RADIO** increase after adjustment, and it was only here that the **RADIO** variables entered our models. In all the other cases, **RADIO** exerted minute effects and, indeed, entered none of the corresponding models.

In conclusion, radio lessons have a strong effect on posttest score, but a relatively weak effect on all the other outcome variables. These other outcome variables may well be beyond the influence of the method of instructional presentation of a single school subject. The decision to fail a student is the decision of the teacher based not only on student achievement (in many subjects) but on other factors as well, as discussed in chapter 6. Attendance, dropout, and reenrollment decisions also involve other factors such as family needs. (The slightly more powerful effect of radio in Grade 3 may be evidence that these external factors play a weaker role in higher grades.) We believe, therefore, that the merits of radio instruction should be judged by its effect on the variable that most directly measures its influence, namely, posttest score. Improvement in the quality of instruction in school is an outcome that is widely believed to be socially desirable in itself. Radio mathematics lessons make a clear contribution to this goal.

REFERENCES

Draper, N., & Smith, H. *Applied regression analysis.* New York: Wiley, 1966.
Jamison, D. Radio education and student repetition. In P. Suppes, B. Searle, & J. Friend (Eds.), *The Radio Mathematics Project: Nicaragua, 1976–1977.* Stanford, Calif.: Stanford University, Institute for Mathematical Studies in the Social Sciences, 1978.
Searle, B., Sheehan, J., González, J., & George, E. Patterns of promotion and wastage for Nicaraguan first-grade students. In P. Suppes, B. Searle, & J. Friend (Eds.), *The Radio Mathematics Project: Nicaragua, 1976–1977.* Stanford, Calif.: Stanford University, Institute for Mathematical Studies in the Social Sciences, 1978.
Wiley, D. Another hour, another day: Quality of schooling, a potent path for policy. In W. H. Sewell (Ed.), *Schooling and achievement in American society.* New York: Academic Press, 1976.

In Nicaragua, whether or not a child is promoted at the end of the school year is entirely in the purview of the teacher. Although the child's achievement level at the end of the year is certainly one of the factors that influence the teacher's decisions, it was shown in the last chapter that interventions that clearly increase the child's achievement do not necessarily increase his chances for promotion. What, then, are the factors that the teacher takes into account in deciding which children to promote? This question is addressed in this chapter, which presents the results of a novel and informative investigation into the determinants of teachers' pass-fail decisions.

Chapter 6

TEACHERS' PROMOTION DECISIONS IN NICARAGUAN FIRST THROUGH FOURTH GRADES

KLAUS GALDA AND JOSÉ GONZÁLEZ

THE RADIO MATHEMATICS PROJECT has for the last several years been investigating teaching in Nicaraguan primary-school classrooms. Although the emphasis of the project has been on the development of an instructional program, many kinds of data about the students, teachers, and Nicaraguan school system have been collected. Recently, an effort has been made to understand the dynamics of educational wastage, that is, the patterns of promotion, repetition, and dropout among primary-school children (see Searle, Sheehan, González, & George, 1978; Jamison, 1978; and chaps. 5 and 7 in this volume).

The Nicaraguan school system's promotion policy is summarized by Searle et al. (1978). The Ministry of Education requires that children attend two-thirds of the school year. If a child meets the attendance requirement, a teacher must base his or her pass-fail decision on class work and final examination results. In other words,

> Promotion from one grade to the next, although guided by regulations promulgated by the Ministry of Education, ultimately rests with the classroom teacher. (pp. 224–225)

Therefore, two determinants of educational wastage are the strategies used by classroom teachers in making promotion (pass-fail) decisions and the teacher and student characteristics influencing these decisions.

In principle, Nicaraguan primary-school teachers base their promotion decisions on attendance and achievement. Searle et al. conclude, however, that these are not the only characteristics influencing teachers' promotion decisions in Nicaraguan first-grade classes. They

179

found that, in addition to achievement, a student's age was strongly related to promotion. Older first-grade students were more likely to be promoted than otherwise comparable younger first-grade students. Also, rural first-grade students were less likely to be promoted than similar urban first-grade students. Commenting on the latter finding, Searle et al. concluded that rural teachers tend to fail more students than their urban colleagues (p. 245). Finally, they found that, contrary to the official regulations, a poor attendance record "does not make promotion impossible" (p. 244).

This chapter reports on a follow-up investigation of the promotion practices described by Searle et al. Specifically, by surveying first-through fourth-grade teachers, this investigation attempts to describe more completely the student and teacher characteristics influencing pass-fail decisions.

The work reported in this chapter extends previous work in three ways:

1. More grade levels are included,
2. teachers are specifically asked about their promotion policies and practices, and
3. teachers are asked to make a pass-fail decision for each of a set of hypothetical students presented to them.

In particular, first- through fourth-grade teachers were invited to respond to a pair of survey instruments—a questionnaire and a set of three lists of hypothetical students. In this manner we hoped to describe the effects of student characteristics other than attendance and achievement on the promotion decisions of Nicaraguan classroom teachers, the effects of teacher characteristics on promotion practices, and the stability of these effects in different contexts, that is, in different grades and regions.

1. THE SURVEY INSTRUMENTS

Two survey instruments were used in the promotion practices study: a five-part questionnaire and a set of three lists of hypothetical students. Both instruments were presented to the teachers in a single package of materials and at a single session. The five-part questionnaire preceded the three lists of hypothetical students.

The Questionnaire

The full text of the questionnaire is presented in Appendix A. Part A of the questionnaire collected demographic data from each teacher: grade, region, sex, age, years of education, teaching experience, etc. Parts B through D asked the teachers about their final-examination policy, their promotion criteria, the Ministry of Education promotion requirements, and the influence of attendance on their promotion decisions. Part E asked them to provide recent promotion, dropout, and repetition data from their school records.

Hypothetical Class Registers

The first list of hypothetical students was in the form of a class register. The teachers were told that these students represented the marginal students in the class and were asked to recommend promoting (passing) or failing each of the students.

As a result of the previously cited work on educational wastage, we were interested in the effect of five student variables on teachers' pass-fail decisions: the student's sex (**SSEX**), age (**SAGE**), repetition history (**REP**), attendance (**ATT**), and achievement (**ACH**) record. The range of values for each of these variables and their definitions are shown in Table 1. These variables were used as follows to generate the first list of hypothetical students.

1. All of the possible combinations of the variable values were generated. This resulted in 270 (2×5×3×3×3) student cases.

2. Impossible or unrealistic cases were eliminated. As a result, nine combinations of **SAGE** and **REP** (i.e., young repeaters and old nonrepeaters) were eliminated.

3. All cases of high attendance and achievement (i.e., **ATT** = 2 and **ACH** = 2) were eliminated. It was assumed that all the teachers would pass students with these characteristics regardless of the values of the other variables. Ninety-six of the 270 ([2×5×3×3×3] − [2×9×9] − [2×6×1]) possible combinations remained after steps 2 and 3.

4. To make the number of hypothetical students more manageable, half of the older repeating students were eliminated. Seventy-two (96 − 1/2×[2×3×8] = 96−24 = 72) hypothetical students remained.

5. Twenty-four of the 72 hypothetical students were randomly selected (without replacement) for each class register. (Each teacher was given a unique class register.)

The basic list of 72 hypothetical students and their respective characteristics was exactly the same for each of the four grades except that each student's age was adjusted accordingly. For example, a student might appear on the class registers presented to teachers in each of the four grades with exactly the same characteristics except that his age is 8 years old in first grade, 9 in second grade, 10 in third grade, and 11 in fourth grade. The distribution of variable values appearing in all the class registers is also presented in Table 1.

The instructions for the hypothetical class register gave only minimal guidelines to the teachers about making their pass-fail decisions. (See translation in Appendix A.) The Ministry regulations were not

TABLE 1

Definitions and Distribution of Variables
Describing Hypothetical Students

Student variable	Definition of value	Distribution of variable values in class registers
SSEX	0 = female	.489
	1 = male	.511
SAGE	0 = basic age (i.e., minimum age for the grade)	.221
	1 = one year older	.441
	2 = two years older	.114
	3 = three years older	.114
	4 = four years older	.109
REP	0 = nonrepeater	.442
	1 = one-time repeater	.220
	2 = two-time repeater	.338
ATT	0 = low attendance (90 days/year)	.364
	1 = middle attendance (120 days/year)	.385
	2 = high attendance (170 days/year)	.251
ACH	0 = low achievement (7.20 average)	.364
	1 = middle achievement (7.50 average)	.377
	2 = high achievement (7.80 average)	.259

given. However, the teachers were told that a school year consisted of 180 school days.

Student achievement information was provided to the teachers by final grades in mathematics, language, science, and social studies. The student achievement variable (**ACH**) used in the analysis below is determined by the researchers from these grades and is merely a convenient way of assigning a general achievement level to each student. It was not explicitly given to the teachers.

Initially, a final grade corresponding to the student's achievement level was going to be assigned to each subject matter; 7.20, 7.50, and

8.00 for **ACH** = 0, 1, and 2, respectively. However, Nicaraguan teachers working with the project suggested that this was too artificial and many teachers might, to appear consistent, feel bound to uniformly pass or fail all students at a given level.[1] Instead, 10 different combinations of grades were generated for each achievement level under the restriction that the average grade of each combination would be the same for each achievement level; 7.20 for **ACH** = 0, 7.50 for **ACH** = 1, and 8.00 for **ACH** = 2. Each student was randomly assigned one of these 10 grade combinations corresponding to his or her randomly assigned achievement level. (It is assumed that teachers place equal weight on the four subjects. Future analyses of the promotion data will investigate the validity of this assumption.)

In summary, the hypothetical class registers of 24 students presented to teachers were designed to be as realistic as possible, presenting cases in a format that the teacher was likely to encounter in the classroom. Part of a hypothetical class register presented to a first-grade teacher is shown in Figure 1. (Note that the sex of the student is not stated explicitly but is implicit in the name.)

Forced-choice Student Lists

To maximize the plausibility of the lists of hypothetical students in the class registers, not all possible combinations of **SAGE** and **REP** were included. (Of course, this is also the case in an actual classroom.) In order to disentangle the relative effects of a student's age and

FIRST GRADE

Name	Age	Repetition	Attendance (days)	Final grades				Pass/ fail
				Mathematics	Language	Science	Social studies	
1. Inés	11	2 times	120	7.20	7.20	7.30	7.10	____
2. Clarisa	7	None	170	7.40	7.50	7.80	7.30	____
3. Napoleón	7	None	120	8.00	8.00	7.90	8.10	____
4. Sergio	9	2 times	120	7.80	7.40	7.60	7.20	____
5. Claudio	8	1 time	120	7.10	7.00	7.30	7.40	____

FIGURE 1. Part of a hypothetical class register presented to a first-grade teacher.

---

[1] Nicaraguan teachers consider 7.50 a failing grade and 7.51 a passing grade.

repetition history, two additional lists of students were presented to the teachers. The students in these lists varied only with regard to their sex (again, not explicitly stated, but implied in the name of the student), age, and repetition history. All of these students were middle achievers with identical final grades and middle attendance records. The repetition history was not given as the number of repetitions, as before, but simply by stating whether the student was a repeater or not. Teachers were asked to pass exactly half of the students in each list and fail the other half. All the teachers responded to the same lists except that the ages were once again different for each grade (i.e., in each successive grade the "same" student was one year older).

Table 2 presents the first list of six students and their characteristics. These students are paired, with each pair differing by only one characteristic. Thus the first two students differ only in age, as do the third and fourth. (Recall that the value of zero for age here appears to the teacher as the minimum legal age for that grade; the value of two is two years older than the minimum legal age.) The first and third students differ only in sex, as do the second and fourth and also the fifth and sixth. The second and fifth differ only in repetition history, as do the fourth and sixth.

Originally, each teacher was to be presented with a list of these pairs and forced to choose between the two students. It was decided

TABLE 2

Sex, Age, and Repetition History
of Students in Forced-choice Situation

Name of student	Sex	Age[a]	Repetition history
Aldo	Male	0	No
Mateo	Male	2	No
Norma	Female	0	No
Alba	Female	2	No
Róger	Male	2	Yes
Mirna	Female	2	Yes

[a] Years older than basic age.

that this approach was not subtle enough. Some teachers might consider it insulting to be forced to choose, for example, between two students who are identical in all respects except for sex. Even at best, the situation is rather artificial. However, it was hoped that presenting a list of six students and asking teachers to pass exactly three, posed the problem in a more reasonable way.

The third and final list consisted of two students who were identical in all respects except that one was an older nonrepeater (Pablo) and the other a younger repeater (Raúl). Both of these students were male with middle attendance and achievement records. By forcing teachers to pass one of these students and fail the other we hoped to differentiate between the relative effects of age and repetition, which are generally seen as one compound effect.

2. DESCRIPTION OF THE TEACHER SAMPLE

The teachers participating in the survey were chosen from lists of teachers who had previously worked with the Radio Mathematics Project. All taught one of the first four grades. Some had worked with radio; others were in project control groups. These teachers had originally been chosen to participate in the radio or control group by random sampling stratified by political department and urbanization (Searle, Matthews, Suppes, & Friend, 1978). All the teachers in a given group (e.g., the 1977 third-grade radio group) were invited to attend a three-hour session to respond to the questionnaire and hypothetical student lists. One hundred twenty teachers were invited to participate, of whom 96 responded. The total number of participating teachers, by grade and region, is presented in Table 3. Some teachers completed the questionnaire and hypothetical student lists at group sessions; others completed them at home and delivered them to the project office. Teachers were paid $7, about one day's salary, for participating in the study.

Descriptive statistics for the teachers completing the survey instruments are presented in Table 4. In summary, the typical respondent was a female teacher (88% female vs. 22% male), approximately 32 years of age (the median age is 28), with 12 years of education (through high school or normal school in the Nicaraguan educational system) and 11 years of teaching experience.

Regional (urban/rural) and grade differences in the teacher sample are presented in Table 5. With respect to grade, the sample of teachers may be divided into two groups: Teachers in the lower grades (i.e., first and second grade) are older (especially in second grade), less educated, and more experienced than teachers in the

TABLE 3

Number of Teachers Responding
to Questionnaire by Grade and Region

Grade/ region	Number of teachers
First	34
Rural	15
Urban	19
Second	22
Rural	7
Urban	15
Third	15
Rural	9
Urban	6
Fourth	25
Rural	11
Urban	14
TOTAL	96
Rural	42
Urban	54

TABLE 4

Characteristics of Teachers
Responding to Questionnaire

Teacher characteristic	Range	Mean	Standard deviation
Sex (**SEX**)	0(F) – 1(M)	.22	.42
Age (**AGE**), in years	18 – 65	31.9	9.9
Education (**TED**), in years	5 – 17	12.2	2.6
Teaching experience (**TEXP**), in years	1 – 48	10.8	9.3

TABLE 5

Characteristics of Teachers
Responding to Questionnaire
by Grade and Region

Teacher characteristic/ grade	Mean		Total
	Rural	Urban	
Sex	.33	.13	.22
First	.33	.11	.21
Second	.29	.07	.14
Third	.44	.17	.33
Fourth	.27	.21	.24
Age	31.5	32.3	31.9
First	32.2	30.5	31.3
Second	35.3	39.1	38.0
Third	31.8	30.5	31.3
Fourth	28.3	28.4	28.3
Education	11.7	12.6	12.2
First	10.2	12.4	11.4
Second	12.7	11.7	12.0
Third	12.6	14.0	13.1
Fourth	12.5	13.3	13.0
Teaching experience	9.9	11.6	10.8
First	11.9	11.9	11.9
Second	11.1	16.1	14.5
Third	10.0	10.7	10.3
Fourth	6.2	7.0	6.6

upper grades (i.e., third and fourth grades). There is a larger percentage of female teachers in the lower grades. With respect to region, urban and rural teachers are approximately the same age, while rural teachers are slightly less educated and experienced than urban teachers. Again, both rural and urban teachers are predominantly female, but more so in the urban areas. Similar differences between lower- and upper-grade teachers are present within each region; similar regional differences exist within each group of grades.

3. QUESTIONNAIRE RESULTS

In this section we summarize the responses made by teachers to a small subsample of the questionnaire items. These items are concerned with the relation between final examinations (as a proxy for achievement), attendance, and pass-fail decisions; other promotion criteria used by teachers; and their awareness and enforcement of the official Ministry of Education promotion regulations.

Final Examinations and Promotion

The teachers responding to the questionnaire use similar procedures with regard to administering final examinations. In summary, almost all of the teachers give self-prepared final examinations in each of the four basic subject areas: mathematics, language, natural science, and social studies. (Agriculture is also tested by about half the teachers.) These final examinations are usually given on different days. A student may take a make-up examination if he or she is absent on one of these days. However, the absence must be justified (e.g., by illness).

About 56% of the teachers surveyed said they required a student to pass all of the final examinations; 28% required a student to pass three out of four, while 16% were more lenient. Lower-grade and rural teachers require fewer final examinations. However, almost all teachers allow a student who fails one or more of the final examinations to take a make-up examination and to be promoted if he passes it. Less than 20% would pass a student who fails the make-up examination.

Despite the apparent strictness expressed by a majority of the teachers with regard to final examinations and promotion, most also agree that it is possible for a student to be promoted without taking the final examinations. However, only half report ever having done so. According to most of the written comments, absence from the final examinations must be excused and the student must have otherwise good achievement (as measured by monthly tests, homework, etc.) and attendance. Another method mentioned for promoting a student who did not take the final examinations is to secure the permission of the school principal.

Attendance and Promotion

As is the case with final examinations, there is general agreement among the teachers surveyed regarding the importance of regular school attendance. Almost all of the teachers think it is important to take attendance every day and report doing so. Furthermore, regular attendance is considered a requirement for promotion. However, only slightly more than half of the teachers report that they have a specific minimum attendance requirement. In addition, 70% of the teachers (and significantly more male than female teachers—$p < .05$) think that it is possible for a student with irregular attendance to be promoted; 75% of the teachers have promoted at least one student with good achievement and poor attendance. Hence, unlike achievement on the final examinations, attendance seems to be a flexible and subjective promotion requirement.

Other Promotion Criteria

Teachers were also asked to list the criteria, in addition to performance on final examinations (i.e., achievement) and attendance, that they use to make pass-fail decisions. One-third of the teachers listed classroom behavior and participation. Age was listed by only 10% of the teachers.

To investigate the relative importance of these promotion criteria, each teacher was asked to list in order of importance all the factors that influence his or her pass-fail decisions. Each factor was assigned a number of points according to its place on the list; first in importance received five points, second four points, third three points, fourth two points, and less than fourth one point. According to the teachers surveyed, the four most influential promotion criteria and their total points are:

Factor	Total points
Achievement	402
Conduct and behavior	248
Effort and participation	229
Attendance	141

Achievement was listed as an influential factor by 90% of the teachers, whereas attendance was listed by only half of the teachers.

Ministry of Education Promotion Requirements

One of the purposes of the questionnaire was to judge the teachers' awareness of the official Ministry of Education promotion regulations. The teachers were specifically asked to list these regulations.

TABLE 6

Ministry of Education Promotion Regulations
as Reported by Teachers

Type of regulation	Number (%) of teachers	
Neither achievement nor attendance	2	(2.2)
Attendance only	3	(3.2)
Achievement only	51	(54.8)
Achievement and attendance	29	(31.2)
Achievement, attendance, and ...	8	(8.6)
TOTAL	96 (100.0)	

Their responses fall into five groups, shown in Table 6. A majority of the teachers listed achievement but not attendance. The next largest group of teachers listed both an achievement and attendance requirement, closely approaching the correct Ministry of Education promotion regulations. However, the diversity of specific achievement and attendance requirements listed was quite marked, ranging from "a majority of classes passed" to "all classes passed," and from "70% attendance" to "100% attendance." Strictly speaking, therefore, few of the teachers know the Ministry regulations. In addition, it is again apparent that the vast majority of teachers emphasize achievement over attendance despite the official parity of these criteria.

In summary, the teachers responding to the questionnaire view achievement as more important than attendance, have more specific criteria relating achievement to promotion than attendance to promotion, and, finally, report applying the achievement criteria more consistently and objectively. Very few of the teachers can report correctly the Ministry of Education promotion regulations.

4. STUDENT CHARACTERISTICS
AND TEACHERS' PASS DECISIONS

The percentages of pass recommendations made by all the teachers for each of the student characteristics in the hypothetical class register are presented in Table 7. (For convenience, in the discussion that follows, pass recommendations will be called pass decisions.) Almost 40% of the decisions made were pass decisions.[2] In general, relatively more pass decisions were made for older, repeating (especially multiple repeaters), and higher achievement students. The sex of the student is generally unrelated to pass-fail decisions. The percentages of pass decisions made for low- and middle-attendence

TABLE 7

Percentage of Teachers' Pass Decisions
for Hypothetical Students
by Student Characteristics

Student characteristic	% pass decisions
Sex	
Female	39.3
Male	37.8
Age	
Basic age	34.1
One year older	35.5
Two years older	47.0
Three years older	41.6
Four years older	48.1
Repetition	
Nonrepeater	34.3
One-time repeater	36.4
Two-time repeater	45.5
Attendance	
Low attendance	42.1
Middle attendance	47.4
High attendance	19.9
Achievement	
Low achievement	8.1
Middle achievement	28.4
High achievement	96.3
TOTAL	38.6

[2] The hypothetical class register is not intended to represent a real class, as we are primarily interested in the marginal students. Therefore, this result should not be interpreted to mean that 40% of the students would pass in a real class.

students are larger than that for students with high attendance records. This is an artificial result due to the exclusion of high-achievement students with high attendance records from the hypothetical class registers presented to the teachers. The effect of attendance within the low- and middle-achievement groups of students is discussed below.

For convenience, the original student variables may be grouped and redefined. The results presented in Table 7 indicate that the effect of student age on promotion is constant for older students. In effect, student age is acting as a dichotomous variable; students two or more years older than basic age are promoted more often than students of basic age or one year older than basic age. The repetition history and attendance variables may also be dichotomized according to whether a student is a repeater or meets the Ministry of Education minimum attendance requirement. Thus, the new student variables are as follows:

Student variable	Definition
NSAGE	0 if **SAGE** = 0 or 1
	1 if **SAGE** = 2, 3, or 4
NREP	0 if **REP** = 0
	1 if **REP** = 1 or 2
NATT	0 if **ATT** = 0
	1 if **ATT** = 1 or 2

The percentages of pass decisions made by all teachers for the redefined student variables are presented in Table 8. In general, significantly more pass decisions ($p < .001$) are made for older and repeating students (regardless of their achievement level).

The differential effect of attendance and each of the other student variables within each achievement group is also presented in Table 8. Attendance is directly related to the percentage of pass decisions for each of the achievement groups. A student is more likely to be promoted if he or she meets the Ministry's minimum attendance requirement. However, the unaggregated data (not presented here) show that the influence of attendance is less once the student has met the minimum attendance requirement; there is relatively little increase in the percentage of pass decisions from **ATT** = 1 to **ATT** = 2 compared to that from **ATT** = 0 to **ATT** = 1 in either the low- or middle-achievement groups. In summary, attendance beyond the

TABLE 8

Percentage of Teachers' Pass Decisions
by Student Characteristics and Achievement Level

Student characteristic	% pass decisions			
	Achievement level			Total
	Low	Middle	High	
Sex				
Female	8.0	30.4	96.7	39.3
Male	8.1	26.2	95.9	37.8
Age				
Young	4.0	23.3	95.5	35.0
Old	16.0***	38.4***	97.9	45.5***
Repetition				
Nonrepeater	3.5	20.5	95.3	34.3
Repeater	11.6***	34.6***	97.1	41.9***
Attendance				
Not eligible	4.6	24.9	94.2	42.1
Eligible	9.7**	30.0	98.3*	36.5
TOTAL	8.1	28.4	96.3	38.6

* $p < .05$.
** $p < .01$.
*** $p < .001$.

minimum requirement will not substantially increase a student's chances of promotion.

The same relations found between a student's sex, age, repetition history, and teacher promotion decision for all the students are present in each of the achievement groups. A student's sex makes essentially no difference in his or her chances of being passed in any of the three achievement groups. Significantly more pass decisions ($p < .001$) are made for older and repeating students in both the low- and middle-achievement groups. Although the effects of these variables on the percentage of pass decisions for high-achievement students are not statistically significant, significantly more pass decisions ($p < .05$) are made for high-achievement students meeting the minimum attendance requirement. However, since practically all of these students are passed regardless of their other characteristics, the statistical significance of additional attendance is not interesting.

The statistical significance of any of the differences in the low and high achievement groups is an artifact of the extremely small variances (.074 and .036, respectively) of the percentages of pass decisions for these groups compared to that for the middle-achievement group of students (.203). The small variances in the percentages of pass decisions for these groups of students are indicative of the extent to which teachers agree to fail low-achievement and pass high-achievement students. Consequently, the discussion that follows will concentrate on the marginal (i.e., middle-achievement) students.

The Relationships Between Student Characteristics, Grade, Region, and Teachers' Pass Decisions

Table 9 presents the percentages of pass decisions made for marginal students for the four student variables—sex, age, repetition, and attendance—by teachers in each group of grades and each region. In general, significantly more upper-grade ($p < .05$) and rural ($p < .01$) teachers make pass decisions regardless of the student characteristics. Consistent with previous findings, a student's sex is not significantly related to his or her chances of being promoted by teachers in either group of grades or region. In contrast, significantly more pass decisions are made for older and repeating students by teachers in both lower ($p < .01$) and upper ($p < .001$) grades, and rural ($p < .001$) and urban ($p < .05$ and $p < .01$ for older and repeating students, respectively) regions. It seems that a student's age is particularly important to upper-grade and rural teachers.

Relative Effects of a Student's Sex, Age, and Repetition

We turn now to an examination of responses to the forced-choice lists. The results presented in Tables 10 and 11 include only those teachers who followed the instructions for the forced-choice lists of students by passing exactly half of them and failing the other half. Only 75 of the 96 teachers followed the instructions for the second list of six students, whereas 85 followed the instructions for the final pair of students. Some teachers failed all of these students. Apparently some of the teachers did not read (or understand) the instructions for this section; others seemed to understand but chose not to follow them.

Table 10 indicates that other things being equal for these six marginal students, sex has no statistically significant effect. Thus, there is little difference between the percentages of teachers passing Aldo and Norma, Mateo and Alba, or Róger and Mirna.

TABLE 9

Percentage of Pass Decisions by Student Characteristic, Grade, and Region for Marginal[a] Students

Student characteristic	% pass decisions			
	Grade		Region	
	Lower	Upper	Rural	Urban
Student's sex				
Female	27.3	34.9	35.5	26.5
Male	23.8	30.3	32.0	22.0
Student's age				
Young	21.3	26.3	26.0	21.2
Old	33.7**	45.8***	49.2***	30.2*
Repetition				
Nonrepeater	18.5	23.5	24.2	17.8
Repeater	30.9**	40.6***	41.4***	29.4**
Attendance				
Not eligible	24.8	25.0	26.9	23.2
Eligible	25.9	36.4*	37.3*	24.7
TOTAL	25.5	32.7	33.8	24.3

Note. Significant lower-upper differences: TOTAL ($p < .05$); Older ($p < .05$); Repeater ($p < .05$); Eligible ($p < .01$). Significant rural-urban differences: TOTAL ($p < .01$); Female ($p < .05$); Male ($p < .05$); Older ($p < .01$); Repeater ($p < .01$); Eligible ($p < .001$).

[a] **ACH** = 1.
* $p < .05$.
** $p < .01$.
*** $p < .001$.

Age does indeed make a great difference (other things being equal). Older students are significantly more likely ($p < .001$) to be passed than younger students. This effect is seen by comparing the percentages of teachers passing Aldo and Mateo, and also Norma and Alba.

Repetition also makes a significant difference, as can be seen by comparing Mateo and Róger ($p < .05$) and also Alba and Mirna ($p < .01$). As noted both here and above, and in Searle, Sheehan, González, and George (1978), teachers tend to pass older students more than younger students and to pass repeaters more than nonrepeaters.

TABLE 10

Percentage of Pass Decisions
for Students in Forced-choice Situation

Name of student	Sex	Age[a]	Repetition history	% pass decisions
Aldo	Male	0	No	20.0
Mateo	Male	2	No	57.3
Norma	Female	0	No	21.3
Alba	Female	2	No	52.0
Róger	Male	2	Yes	74.7
Mirna	Female	2	Yes	76.0

[a] Years older than basic age.

TABLE 11

Percentage of Pass Decisions for
Old Nonrepeater Versus Young Repeater

Student	% pass decisions
Old nonrepeater (Pablo)	67.9
Young repeater (Raúl)	32.1

The relative effects of age and repetition are directly compared by the second forced-choice list (see Table 11). In general, the effect of age is significantly greater ($p < .001$) than that of repetition. In this forced-choice situation, about two-thirds of the teachers passed the older nonrepeater and only one-third passed the younger repeater.

Relative Effects of Student's Sex, Age, and Repetition
in Different Grades and Regions

Tables 12 and 13 present the results of the forced-choice lists by grade and region. In general, the same relative effects of sex, age, and repetition are found in each group of grades and in each region. There are no significant differences in the percentages of pass decisions made by teachers in either group of grades or in either region for male and female students. All of the differences in the percentages of pass decisions for older students are significant ($p \leq .05$). As was found with the hypothetical class registers, student age appears to be a more important factor in the rural areas.

There are no significant differences in the percentages of pass decisions with respect to repetition in the lower grades. However, significantly more pass decisions are made for repeaters in both rural ($p < .05$) and urban ($p < .05$ for female repeaters) regions, and in upper grades ($p < .01$). Repetition, therefore, is of primary concern to upper-grade teachers. Finally, there are no statistically significant differences between groups of grades or between regions.

TABLE 12

Percentage of Pass Decisions by Grade and Region
for Students in Forced-choice Situation

Name of student	Sex	Age[a]	Repetition history	% pass decisions			
				Grade		Region	
				Lower ($N = 42$)	Upper ($N = 33$)	Rural ($N = 35$)	Urban ($N = 40$)
Aldo	Male	0	No	23.8	15.2	17.1	22.5
Mateo	Male	2	No	61.9	51.5	57.1	57.5
Norma	Female	0	No	23.8	18.2	17.1	25.0
Alba	Female	2	No	54.8	48.5	54.3	50.0
Róger	Male	2	Yes	69.0	81.8	80.0	70.0
Mirna	Female	2	Yes	69.0	84.8	77.1	75.0

[a] Years older than basic age.

TABLE 13

Percentage of Pass Decisions by Grade and Region
for Old Nonrepeater Versus Young Repeater

| | % pass decisions | | | |
| | Grade | | Region | |
Student	Lower (N = 48)	Upper (N = 36)	Rural (N = 38)	Urban (N = 46)
Old nonrepeater (Pablo)	72.9	61.1	71.1	65.2
Young repeater (Raúl)	27.1	38.9	28.9	34.8

Table 13 indicates that the primacy of age over repetition is present in both groups of grades (p < .001 in lower and p < .05 in upper grades) and in both regions (p < .001 in rural and p < .01 in urban areas).

A Partial Ordering of Student Characteristics

A substantial majority (85%) of the teachers questioned reported that there is an upper limit to the number of students who may be promoted in their school or classroom. This percentage of teachers is slightly higher in the rural regions and lower grades.

Robinson (1977) and Jamison (1978) argue that the lack of places in grades higher than the first, resulting in de facto promotion quotas, may cause teachers to fail students. Consequently, a student's relative rather than absolute achievement level, for example, becomes a determining factor in his or her promotion (Jamison, 1978, p. 212). Similarly, a student's age as such does not influence a teacher's promotion decision. Age is an influential factor only if the student is *older* or *younger* than the majority of the students in the class.

One possible model of a teacher's promotion decision is the filling of a quota from a rank-ordered list of students. The list is produced by ordering students by sex, age, repetition history, attendance record, and achievement level (in our hypothetical list—the actual classroom situation may involve other variables). Once the students are ordered (from 1 to n for a classroom with n students) and the maximum number (i) of students to be promoted is known, it is easily determined which students will be promoted (students 1 through i).[3]

This promotion decision process can be represented by a decision tree that orders student characteristics according to how teachers use them to distinguish among students. A variable's power to distinguish among students may be measured by the range of the percentages of the teacher's pass decisions it produces; the greatest range indicates the greatest distinguishing effect of that variable at that point in the teacher's decision process. For example, as shown in Table 14, at the outset the range for achievement is much larger than for other variables, so it is used first. After the first student variable has entered into the decision process, the percentage ranges for other variables are recalculated given the values of the first variable. In this manner, the differential effects of the subsequent student variables on individual values of the first may be assessed. For example, it may be that a student's sex is more important in passing an older middle-achievement student than a younger student with comparable achievement.

Table 14 presents the step-by-step results of such a procedure. Achievement, as expected, is the first student characteristic to enter into a teacher's promotion decision. As has been noted above, almost all the teachers failed low-achievement students and passed high-achievement students. These two types of students will go at the bottom and top, respectively, of the promotion list. The greatest differential effect of the other student variables will occur for the middle or marginal group of students. Therefore, only middle-achievement students are considered in steps 2 to 4 of Table 14.

In our model, age is the second characteristic to be considered by a teacher deciding to pass or fail a marginal student; it is chosen because the range, 15.1, is larger than for other variables. The ranges for step 3 of the promotion decision process indicate that a student's repetition history is the third characteristic to be considered in the promotion decisions for young middle-achievement students. However, because of the limitations imposed by our construction of the class lists on the values of **NREP** for certain values of **NSAGE** (see p. 181), all older middle-achievers have the same repetition history. That is, an older student's repetition history is constant (in our list) and cannot, therefore, affect a teacher's pass-fail decision for these students. It will not be included in the promotion decision model for

---

[3] We do not suggest that the teacher consciously organizes promotion decisions in this way, but it is an interesting way to view the process and see the relative importance of each of our variables.

Distinguishing Power of Student Variables
in Teacher Promotion Decisions

Step in decision process	Student variable	Range[a] in percentage of teachers' pass decisions
Step 1		
	ACH	88.2
	NATT	5.6
	NREP	7.6
	NSAGE	10.5
	SSEX	1.5
Step 2 **ACH** = 1		
	NATT	5.1
	NREP	14.1
	NSAGE	15.1
	SSEX	4.2
Step 3 **ACH** = 1 **NSAGE** = 0		
	NATT	3.2
	NREP	8.2
	SSEX	5.1
NSAGE = 1		
	NATT	7.1
	NREP	(no range)
	SSEX	.8
Step 4 **ACH** = 1 **NSAGE** = 0 **NREP** = 0		
	NATT	1.8
	SSEX	5.8
NREP = 1		
	NATT	6.2
	SSEX	4.2
NSAGE = 1 **NATT** = 0		
	NREP	(no range)
	SSEX	5.5
NATT = 1		
	NREP	(no range)
	SSEX	1.9

[a] Range = % PASS $_{max}$ − % PASS $_{min}$.

older students. Thus, an older student's attendance record is the third variable to enter into a teacher's promotion decision.

Sex is the fourth student characteristic to enter into a teacher's promotion decision for young nonrepeaters, and attendance is the fourth characteristic entering into pass-fail decisions for young repeaters. By elimination, the fourth and final characteristic to affect a teacher's promotion decision for older students, regardless of attendance record, is the sex of the student.

The promotion decision tree resulting from our analysis, presented in Figure 2, produces 14 unique groups of students—low achievers, high achievers, and 12 groups of middle achievers grouped and ordered according to their remaining characteristics. In order to test the descriptive power of the decision tree model, the Pearson product-moment correlation (r) was calculated for each classroom between the actual promotion decisions and the promotion decisions assigned to each student by the decision tree.

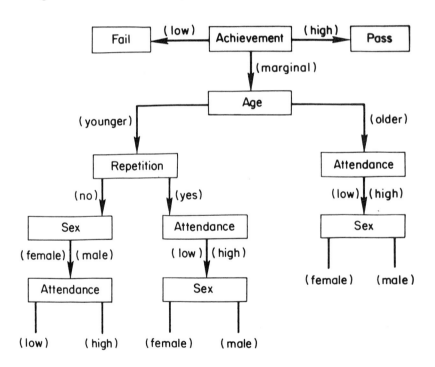

FIGURE 2. Decision tree used in teachers' promotion decisions.

The following procedure was used to analyze the fit of the promotion decision-tree model to actual teacher decisions:

1. Students in each of 30 randomly selected classrooms (i.e., all the promotion decisions made by 30 randomly selected teachers) were rank ordered according to the promotion tree.

2. Each classroom was assigned a quota (i) of students that could be promoted. For our purposes the quota for each classroom was taken to be the number of students actually promoted by the teacher.

3. All students with a ranking less than or equal to the quota were promoted; all students with a ranking greater than the quota were failed.

4. Pearson product-moment correlations were calculated for each classroom between the actual promotion decisions and the promotion decisions predicted by the decision tree.

The mean correlation between the actual promotion decisions and predicted promotion decisions is .75, with the actual correlations ranging from .16 to 1.00. (A correlation of 1.00 was obtained for 11 of the 30 classrooms.) The decision tree correctly predicted 100% of the promotion decisions for high achievers, 93% for low achievers, and 77% for middle achievers in the 30 randomly selected classrooms. These measures indicate that our promotion decision tree is a relatively good predictor of teacher promotion practices. In addition, it indicates that, as for achievement and age, a student's characteristics relative to those of the other students in a classroom (rather than his characteristics considered in isolation) play a determining role in his or her promotion or failure.

Student Characteristics and
Individual Teachers' Promotion Strategies

Another interesting way to look at these data is not in terms of what happens to types of students, but from the point of view of the individual teacher. The promotion strategies of individual teachers, defined with respect to student characteristics, were identified by inspecting each class register. These strategies were classified into eight categories, listed below with the number of teachers in each category. Unless otherwise noted, the teachers in each category pass all high-achievement students.

Strategy	Number of teachers
1. Pass exactly the high-achievement students.	26
2. Same as 1, with one exception.	16

3. Also pass all middle-achievement
    students who do well in
    mathematics or language.   11

4. Pass older middle-achievement
    students who do well in
    mathematics or language.   6

5. Pass all older students.   3

6. Pass only high-achievement
    students who attend at
    least two-thirds of the
    time.   2

7. Other identifiable strategy.   10

8. No identifiable strategy.   22

        TOTAL   96

It seems reasonable to assume that if a teacher appears to be following an obvious strategy and deviates for only one student (out of 24), this represents an error. This assumption was used in classifying some of the teacher strategies.

Almost 45% of the teachers pass high-achievement students exclusively and disregard all other student variables. Another 10% of the teachers also promote all middle-achievement students who pass either mathematics or language (or both). Thus, more than half of the teachers appear to take only achievement into account.

Note that only two of the 96 teachers appear to adhere strictly to the official guidelines by passing only high-achievement students who attend at least 120 days. Approximately one-third of the teachers appear to take some combination of the student variables into account. However, in these cases, either an idiosyncratic strategy or no obvious strategy at all is exhibited by the teachers. Some teachers in the latter category promoted students in a haphazard or sometimes obviously inconsistent way.

5. TEACHER CHARACTERISTICS AND PASS DECISIONS

In order to facilitate a discussion of the relationships between teacher characteristics and pass decisions, the teacher's age, education, and experience variables (i.e., **AGE**, **TED**, and **TEXP**) are grouped and redefined. The new variables, **NTAGE**, **NTED**, and **NTEXP**, are dichotomous and reflect whether the teacher's age, education, or experience is greater or less than (or equal to) the median value for the total sample of teachers. Thus, the new variables are defined as follows:

Variable	Median	New variable
AGE	28	**NTAGE** = 0 if **AGE** $\leq$ 28
		NTAGE = 1 if **AGE** > 28
TED	12	**NTED** = 0 if **TED** $\leq$ 12
		NTED = 1 if **TED** > 12
TEXP	8	**NTEXP** = 0 if **TEXP** $\leq$ 8
		NTEXP = 1 if **TEXP** > 8

The percentages of pass decisions for all the students of the hypothetical class registers for each of the new teacher variables are presented in Table 15. For all the students, relatively more of the pass decisions are made by older, more educated, and more experienced teachers. None of these differences is statistically significant for the total group of hypothetical students. However, a significantly larger percentage of pass decisions ($p < .01$) was made by male than by female teachers.

Teacher Characteristics, Student Achievement,
and Teacher Promotion Decisions

Table 15 also presents the percentages of pass decisions by teacher characteristics and student achievement level. There are no statistically significant differences in the percentages of pass decisions made by teachers with respect to any of the teacher variables for the low-achievement hypothetical students. This is not surprising since, as was noted above, almost all of the teachers agree that these students should be failed regardless of their other characteristics. The relationships found between teacher characteristics (except for age) and pass decisions for the total group of students are also found for low-achievement students.

Similarly, the relationships found between teacher characteristics and pass decisions for high-achievement students are similar to those exhibited for the total group of students regardless of achievement level. Significantly larger percentages of pass decisions were made by male ($p < .001$) and older ($p < .01$) teachers. The statistical sig-

TABLE 15

Percentage of Pass Decisions by Teacher Characteristic
and by Achievement Level of Hypothetical Students

Teacher characteristic	% pass decisions			
	Achievement level			Total
	Low	Middle	High	
Sex				
Female	7.7	24.8	95.3	36.9
Male	9.5	41.9**	100.0**	44.9*
Age				
≤ 28	8.2	27.0	93.8	36.9
> 28	7.9	29.6	98.5*	40.1
Education				
≤ 12	7.6	24.4	95.5	37.2
> 12	8.8	32.0	97.0	40.1
Teaching experience				
≤ 8	7.1	27.5	94.6	37.2
> 8	9.5	28.9	98.4	40.3

* $p < .01$.
** $p < .001$.

nificance of these differences, however, is once again an artifact of the small variance caused by a general agreement among the teachers to promote these students. These results should, therefore, be interpreted cautiously.

The middle-achievement (or marginal) hypothetical students are the most interesting case because of the amount of teacher disagreement over their promotion. One would expect variables other than **ACH** to enter into the pass-fail decisions for these students. The same general promotion trends found for all the students are exhibited by the teachers for middle-achievement students: The percentage of pass decisions made by male teachers, however, is significantly larger ($p < .001$) than that for female teachers.

Teacher Characteristics, Grade, Region,
and Teachers' Pass Decisions

The percentages of teachers' pass decisions in different grades and regions for each value of the teacher variables are presented for the total group and for the marginal hypothetical students in Tables 16 and 17. Table 16 indicates that upper-grade teachers (except male teachers) generally make a larger percentage of pass decisions for the total group of students, significantly so ($p < .05$) for female and experienced teachers. Similarly, rural teachers (except female and older teachers) generally make a larger percentage of pass decisions for the total group of students, significantly so ($p < .05$) for younger and more educated teachers. Table 17 indicates that these same patterns are found in teachers' pass decisions for marginal students.

In summary, the same tendencies found for the total sample of teachers with respect to teacher characteristics are found within each group of grades and within each region. In other words, regardless of the context in which a teacher makes a promotion decision, older,

TABLE 16

Percentage of Pass Decisions by Teacher Characteristic, Grade, and Region for All Hypothetical Students

| Teacher characteristic | % pass decisions | | | |
| | Grade | | Region | |
	Lower	Upper	Rural	Urban
Sex				
Female	34.7	40.2	36.8	37.0
Male	46.5***	43.2	46.4**	41.0
Age				
≤ 28	35.0	39.2	39.8	33.9
> 28	38.6	42.5	40.0	40.1*
Education				
≤ 12	36.0	39.5	37.3	37.1
> 12	38.4	41.8	44.4*	37.7
Teaching experience				
≤ 8	35.5	39.1	39.5	34.8
> 8	38.1	44.6	40.7	40.1

Note. Significant lower-upper differences: Rural ($p < .01$); Female ($p < .05$); Experience > 8 ($p < .05$). Significant rural-urban differences: Upper ($p < .05$); Age ≤ 28 ($p < .05$); Education > 12 ($p < .05$).

* $p < .05$.

** $p < .01$.

*** $p < .001$.

more educated, more experienced, and male teachers make relatively more pass decisions. In addition, although not presented here, the same general tendencies that are found for the entire population of teachers are found in each group of grades within each region. There are no significant differences from the tendencies found for the entire sample of teachers, presented in Table 15: Relatively more pass decisions are made by male (except in the urban upper grades), older (except in the rural upper grades), more educated (except in the rural lower and urban upper grades), and more experienced teachers. The stability of the general promotion tendencies found for the entire group of teachers in each grade-region grouping is remarkable.

TABLE 17

Percentage of Pass Decisions by Teacher Characteristic, Grade, and Region for Marginal[a] Hypothetical Students

Teacher characteristic	% pass decisions			
	Grade		Region	
	Lower	Upper	Rural	Urban
Sex				
Female	22.2	29.2	27.3	23.4
Male	40.7***	43.2*	47.0***	30.9
Age				
≤ 28	27.0	27.1	33.8	20.6
> 28	24.0	39.7*	34.5	26.7
Education				
≤ 12	23.7	26.0	30.9	17.8
> 12	28.7	35.9	37.9	29.1**
Teaching experience				
≤ 8	27.7	27.1	33.5	21.9
> 8	22.0	44.7**	34.4	25.7

Note. Significant lower-upper differences: Female ($p < .05$); Older ($p < .01$); More experienced ($p < .001$). Significant rural-urban differences: Male ($p < .05$); Younger ($p < .01$); Less educated ($p < .01$); Less experienced ($p < .01$).

[a] **ACH** = 1.

* $p < .05$.

** $p < .01$.

*** $p < .001$.

*Interaction of Teacher Characteristics
and Student Characteristics*

A teacher's sex has been found to be significantly related to the percentage of pass decisions made for all the hypothetical students appearing in the class registers. Besides achievement, a student's age and repetition history were also found to be significantly related to the percentage of pass decisions (i.e., the probability that the student will be promoted). Table 18 presents the percentage of pass decisions made for the three student variables—sex, age, and repetition—by female and male teachers, respectively.

Consistent with previous findings, a student's sex is not significantly related to his or her chances of being promoted by either male or female teachers. However, there is a significant tendency ($p < .05$) for male teachers to make relatively more pass decisions for male students than female teachers make. In addition, significantly larger percentages of pass decisions are made by female and male teachers for older ($p < .001$ and $p < .05$, respectively) and repeating ($p < .001$) students. Both female and male teachers tend to favor older and repeating students in their promotion decisions, male

TABLE 18

Percentage of Pass Decisions by Student Characteristic
and Teacher's Sex

Student characteristic	% pass decisions	
	Female teachers	Male teachers
Student's sex		
Female	38.0	44.5
Male	35.8	45.1
Student's age		
Young	34.1	38.3
Old	42.3**	58.4**
Repetition		
Nonrepeater	33.9	36.1
Repeater	39.3*	52.0**

Note. Significant male teacher-female teacher differences: Male students ($p < .05$); Old students ($p < .001$); Repeaters ($p < .001$).

  * $p < .05$.
 ** $p < .001$.

teachers significantly more so ($p < .001$) than their female colleagues.

Teacher Responses to Questionnaire Items
and Pass Decisions

In general, no significant relationships between teacher responses to questionnaire items and the percentage of pass decisions for the marginal or all the hypothetical students were found. For example, approximately the same percentage of pass decisions was made by teachers who said they had promoted students in the past who did not meet promotion requirements and by teachers who said they did not promote such students. Similarly, approximately the same percentage of pass decisions was made by teachers who listed both attendance and achievement requirements (i.e., "know" the Ministry regulations) as by teachers who did not. Finally, although more pass decisions were made for low-attendance and low-achievement students by teachers who did not list attendance or achievement as important factors in their promotion decisions, these differences are not significant. In addition, these trends are reversed for middle- and high-achievement students. In summary, responses to key questionnaire items concerned with past promotion behavior and promotion criteria are not reliable predictors of pass-fail decisions on the hypothetical class registers. There is essentially no difference between the percentage of pass decisions made by teachers who responded affirmatively and negatively to these questionnaire items.

6. CONCLUSIONS

The survey of promotion practices indicates that student achievement is the primary factor in the promotion decisions of Nicaraguan first- through fourth-grade teachers. Teachers appear to have specific and objective criteria relating achievement, as reflected by final examinations, to promotion. Attendance "requirements," however, are flexible and subjectively applied.

The attendance and achievement criteria of individual teachers are formulated in relative ignorance of (or ignoring) the official Ministry of Education promotion regulations. Indeed, only two of the 96 teachers surveyed applied the Ministry of Education promotion regulations to students presented in the hypothetical class register. In both the questionnaire and the hypothetical class lists, teachers emphasize achievement over attendance in opposition to their official parity in the Ministry regulations.

In general, low-achievement students are failed and high-achievement students are promoted. More complex decision processes occur in the case of marginal students. Apart from achievement, a student's age is the only student characteristic that significantly influences the teachers' promotion decisions for marginal students. Older students are promoted significantly more often than younger students. In this respect the findings of Searle, Sheehan, González, and George (1978) with data from actual classes are verified using hypothetical student lists. In addition, the effect of age on teachers' promotion decisions was found to be significantly greater than that of repetition. The results of the hypothetical class lists with respect to age are in opposition to what the teachers report on the questionnaire: Only 10% of the teachers listed the student's age as a significant influence on their promotion decisions. In this respect, teachers may be unaware of the influence of a student's age on their promotion decisions.

The teacher's sex is significantly related to pass-fail decisions. Male teachers make relatively more pass decisions than female teachers. More specifically, male teachers make significantly more pass decisions for male, older, and repeating students than do their female colleagues. In general, therefore, male teachers are less strict in their promotion practices. Finally, though statistically insignificant, the older, more educated, and more experienced teachers tend to make relatively more pass decisions than younger, less educated, and less experienced teachers.

In general, the context in which a promotion decision is made is directly related to the outcome of the decision. The promotion practices survey considered four contexts (i.e., lower and upper grades, and rural and urban regions) and the effect of two sets of variables (i.e., student and teacher characteristics) within these contexts on pass-fail decisions. In summary, relatively more pass decisions are made in upper grades and in rural regions. The former finding may be explained by the relatively larger number of spaces in upper-grade classrooms due to greater wastage in the lower grades. In other words, the failure rate of lower grades is caused by fewer actual places in the next grade, not necessarily poor achievement on the part of the student. The availability of relatively fewer places in the next grade requires (either de facto or de jure) the lower-grade teacher to fail relatively more students than his or her upper-grade colleague.

Some student variables interact with context variables (grade and region) in their effects on teachers' promotion decisions. For example, the effect of student age is different in urban and rural regions. The selective promotion of older students was found to be a more markedly upper-grade and rural phenomenon. In contrast, the effects of teacher characteristics on pass-fail decisions are remarkably stable in different contexts.

The survey of promotion practices has provided us with a more complete description of the dynamics underlying teachers' pass-fail decisions. It has resulted in a description of the promotion decision process characterized by a complex interaction of student, teacher, and contextual variables. Additional investigations should be undertaken to further describe and explain the interactive effects of student, teacher, and contextual variables on teacher pass-fail decisions, to reveal the effects of achievement in specific subject matters on pass-fail decisions, and to verify these findings in larger contexts.

REFERENCES

Jamison, D. Radio education and student repetition. In P. Suppes, B. Searle, & J. Friend (Eds.), *The Radio Mathematics Project: Nicaragua, 1976–1977*. Stanford, Calif.: Stanford University, Institute for Mathematical Studies in the Social Sciences, 1978.

Robinson, B. *El Salvador education sector analysis: Executive summary*. Washington, D.C.: U.S. Agency for International Development, 1977.

Searle, B., Matthews, P., Suppes, P., & Friend, J. Formal evaluation of the 1976 first-grade instructional program. In P. Suppes, B. Searle, & J. Friend (Eds.), *The Radio Mathematics Project: Nicaragua, 1976–1977*. Stanford, Calif.: Stanford University, Institute for Mathematical Studies in the Social Sciences, 1978.

Searle, B., Sheehan, J., González, J., & George, E. Patterns of promotion and wastage for Nicaraguan first-grade students. In P. Suppes, B. Searle, & J. Friend (Eds.), *The Radio Mathematics Project: Nicaragua, 1976–1977*. Stanford, Calif.: Stanford University, Institute for Mathematical Studies in the Social Sciences, 1978.

APPENDIX A

Teachers' Promotion Practices Survey

Introduction

Dear teacher:

As you know, the Radio Mathematics Project has been operating an experimental program with the technical assistance of Stanford University. Our experimental work is extremely important to educational research. One of Stanford's interests has been to understand the problems of the educational system in Nicaragua.

With your cooperation, investigators at Stanford University would like to collect information about the criteria teachers use to promote a student, student repetition, and dropout. For these reasons we ask you to read each question of the attached survey carefully and write as clear and honest an answer as possible.

It goes without saying that the information you give us will go directly to Stanford and will remain strictly confidential.

We thank you for your cooperation.

The Radio Mathematics Project

A. GENERAL INFORMATION

    1. Age: _____

    2. Sex: _____

    3a. Years of education:
    Primary: _____
    Secondary: _____
    Superior: _____
    Other: _____

    b. Where did you receive your teacher training?
_____

c. Explain: Did you graduate? _____
Are you an "empírico"?[1] _____

4a. Years of teaching experience: _____

b. Type of school you teach at:
Urban _____
Rural _____

c. Why are you teaching at this school?

d. Do you enjoy your work?

e. Do you like your present position?

B. FINAL EXAMINATIONS

1. Have you given final examinations to your students in the past? If not, why not?

2. Did you write the final examinations by yourself? If not, explain where you obtained your final examinations, and who wrote the final examinations you gave.

3. In what subjects did you give final examinations? (List the subjects.)

---

[1] An "empírico" in Nicaragua is a noncertificated teacher.

4. Do you give the same final examinations every year?

_____

_____

5. Do you change the final examinations in all subjects? If so, how often do you change them and in what subjects?

_____

_____

6. Are the final examinations of all subjects given the same day?

_____

_____

7. If a student is absent the day of the final examinations, can he take them another day? Explain.

_____

_____

8. Is it possible for a student to be promoted without taking the final examinations? Explain.

_____

_____

9. Have you ever promoted a student who did not take the final examinations?

_____

_____

C. PROMOTION CRITERIA

1. If a student does not take the final examinations what can he do to be promoted?

_____

2a. In how many subject areas do you give final examinations?

b. How many of them does a student have to pass to be promoted to the next grade?

_____

_____

3. Do students who fail the final examinations have an opportunity to take them again?

_____

_____

4. If so, when can a student take the final examinations again?

_____

_____

5a. Are students who pass the make-up examinations promoted?

_____

_____

b. Can students who fail the make-up examinations be promoted?

_____

_____

6. Besides the results of the final examinations, what other factors do you consider in promoting or failing a student?

_____

_____

7a. Do you consider the amount or quality of a student's classroom participation in deciding to promote or fail that student?

_____

_____

b. Do you consider a student's conduct in deciding to promote or fail that student?

_____

_____

8a. Do you consider a student's homework in deciding to promote or fail that student?

_____

_____

b. Do you grade the different activities of a student? Explain.

_____

_____

9. List in the order of importance all the factors that influence your decision to promote or fail a student.

10a. Have you ever promoted a student who failed to meet the requirements for promotion? Explain.

b. Have you ever been forced to fail a student who met the requirements for promotion? Explain.

11. Can you give some examples of factors that have forced you to promote a student who failed to meet the requirements for promotion?

12. Are you the only one responsible for making pass-fail decisions?

13. Has the school director or some other individual helped you make pass-fail decisions? If so, give some examples.

14. What does the Ministry of Education require of a student for you to promote him?

15. Do you think that the majority of teachers abide by these requirements?

16. Does your school director have any additional promotion requirements?

_____

_____

D. **ATTENDANCE**

1. Is regular attendance a requirement for promotion?

_____

_____

2. Is it possible for a student with irregular attendance to be promoted? Explain.

_____

_____

3. Have you ever promoted students with excellent achievement but poor attendance?

_____

_____

4. Do you have a minimum attendance requirement for promotion? If so, what is it?

_____

_____

5. Have you ever promoted students who did not meet this minimum attendance requirement? If so, why?

_____

_____

6. Do you take attendance every day?

_____

_____

7. Do you think it is important to take attendance every day?

_____

_____

8. What do you do on days when there is no regular class? (For
example, rain, field trips, disturbances, etc.)
a. Mark everyone present. _____
b. Mark everyone absent. _____
c. Not take attendance. _____
d. Other. (Explain.)

_____

_____

9. Which Ministry of Public Education attendance requirements
for promotion are used in your school? List them.

_____

10. Do you think that these Ministry of Education requirements
are adequate? Explain.

_____

_____

11. Do you think that a rural primary-school graduate is as well
prepared as an urban primary-school graduate? (Please explain your answer, preferably based on your experience.)

_____

_____

E. **APPROXIMATE DATA FROM
YOUR TEACHING EXPERIENCE**

1. Please fill in the following tables with the information it asks. If
possible, consult your 1976 and 1977 class records. If you no
longer have these records, make an approximation.
a. Number of students in each of the grades you taught in 1976.

	Grade 1	Grade 2	Grade 3	Grade 4	Grade 5	Grade 6
Promoted	___	___	___	___	___	___
Failed	___	___	___	___	___	___
Dropped out	___	___	___	___	___	___

b. Number of students in each of the grades you taught in 1977.

	Grade 1	Grade 2	Grade 3	Grade 4	Grade 5	Grade 6
Promoted	___	___	___	___	___	___
Failed	___	___	___	___	___	___
Dropped out	___	___	___	___	___	___

c. What is the approximate number of students in each grade you are teaching in 1978 who will be promoted, failed, or drop out? (Fill in the following table.)

	Grade 1	Grade 2	Grade 3	Grade 4	Grade 5	Grade 6
Promoted	___	___	___	___	___	___
Failed	___	___	___	___	___	___
Dropped out	___	___	___	___	___	___

2. Is there a maximum number of students who may be promoted in your school? If so, how many students may be promoted in each grade?

_____

_____

3. How many students per class in each grade can be accepted in your school?

	Number of sections	Number of students per section
Grade 1	___	___
Grade 2	___	___
Grade 3	___	___
Grade 4	___	___
Grade 5	___	___
Grade 6	___	___

4. In your school what is the main reason why students drop out?

_____

_____

5a. Do good students drop out?

_____

b. Why do you think the good students drop out?

_____

_____

6a. In what months of the year do most of the dropouts occur?

_____

_____

b. For each of these months give the reasons you think the number of dropouts increases.

_____

_____

7a. What percentage of the students who are absent for several months at a time return to school the same year?

_____

_____

b. What percentage of the students who drop out return to school the next year?

_____

_____

8. What percentage of the children who drop out never return to school?

_____

_____

9. What percentage of the good students who drop out return to school?

_____

_____

10. What percentage of the students in your school transfer to other schools?

_____

_____

On the following pages you will find a class register. It consists of part of a list of children in a class—a class consisting of fictitious students. Assume that the grades given for these 24 children are the final mean grades resulting from the bimonthly and final examinations for each subject. Also assume that, for now, you have no other information about these students on which to base a pass-fail decision.

Assume that in each case the children will not have an opportunity to take a make-up examination.

We would like you to recommend whether each student should be promoted or failed by marking pass or fail in the corresponding boxes of the last column; it does not necessarily have to be a decision, only a recommendation.

It is important that you realize that the final grades in each subject are written out to two decimal places and that the second decimal may be rounded off; as such, the final grade in each case is an approximation. For example, in the subjects where a student has a final grade of 7.50, that is an approximate mean grade. Do not interpret this grade as if the student only needs one hundreth of a point to pass the subject.

In the attendance column, assume that the maximum number of class days in a school year is 180.

(Part of a sample class list)

THIRD GRADE

| Name | Age | Repetition | Attendance (days per year) | Final grades | | | | Pass/fail |
				Mathematics	Language	Science	Social studies	
1. Margarita	12	2 times	120	7.40	7.50	7.80	7.30	____
2. Samuel	10	No	120	8.20	7.90	7.90	8.00	____
			(etc.)					
24. Matilde	10	No	90	8.00	8.00	7.90	8.10	____

With the same promotion criteria you used for the students on the previous pages, we would like you look at the list of students on the next page. Which of the first six students would you recommend for promotion? Select three of these students to be promoted and write the word **promoted** in the last column. For the other three students write **failed**.

Choose one of the last two students, Pablo and Raúl, to be promoted, using the same criteria as before, and fail the other student.

THIRD GRADE

Name	Age	Repeti-tion	Atten-dance (days per year)	Final grades				Pass/fail
				Mathe-matics	Lan-guage	Sci-ence	Social studies	
1. Aldo	9	No	120	7.40	7.60	7.40	7.60	___
2. Mateo	11	No	120	7.40	7.60	7.40	7.60	___
3. Norma	9	No	120	7.40	7.60	7.40	7.60	___
4. Alba	11	No	120	7.40	7.60	7.40	7.60	___
5. Róger	11	Yes	120	7.40	7.60	7.40	7.60	___
6. Mirna	11	Yes	120	7.40	7.60	7.40	7.60	___

Reasons:

_____

_____

_____

_____

Name	Age	Repeti-tion	Atten-dance (days per year)	Final grades				Pass/fail
				Mathe-matics	Lan-guage	Sci-ence	Social studies	
1. Pablo	12	No	120	7.40	7.60	7.40	7.60	____
2. Raúl	10	Yes	120	7.40	7.60	7.40	7.60	____

Reasons:

_____

_____

_____

_____

The elegant and well-fitting models discussed in the last chapter are quite consistent with the hypothesis that Nicaraguan teachers use an implicit quota system in making pass-fail decisions. From those models we could infer that the factor given the most weight by teachers is achievement, but that their concern is with relative achievement rather than achievement in absolute terms. Thus, any intervention, such as radio, that uniformly increases achievement would have no impact on teachers' pass-fail decisions.

This chapter presents a substantiation of the same hypothesis, but uses a completely different kind of analysis of an independent data base.

Chapter 7

RADIO EDUCATION
AND STUDENT FAILURE IN NICARAGUA:
A FURTHER NOTE

DEAN T. JAMISON

The World Bank

PEDAGOGICAL INTERVENTIONS, such as the Radio Mathematics Project in Nicaragua,[1] can be expected to affect not only students' learning, but also their attitudes, their propensity to be promoted from grade to grade, and even, perhaps, their propensity to remain in school. In an earlier paper (Jamison, 1978), I observed that few evaluations of pedagogical interventions have addressed these non-learning outcomes, and, in the context of a broader assessment of the impact of the project, I reported on its effect on student failure propensity. Using data from the preliminary implementation of the radio mathematics lessons at the first-grade level in 1975, I concluded that

> In large part because of their improved mathematics competence, students exposed to radio lessons were considerably less likely to fail first grade than were controls. The estimated probability of failure for students

The author is indebted to Edward I. George and Barbara Searle for valuable conversations concerning this note and to George for his assistance with the statistical analyses. The work reported here was undertaken in part under the auspices of World Bank research project RPO671–54, "The Economics of Educational Radio." The views expressed here are those of the author and do not necessarily reflect those of the World Bank or any other organization.

[1] See Searle, Friend, and Suppes (1976) for a description of the Radio Mathematics Project and of the methods of curriculum design and lesson preparation that were central in its implementation.

exposed to radio was .33; the estimated probability for control students was .45.[2] (p. 219)

My purpose in this further note on the project's impact on student failure in Nicaragua is to examine whether the findings from the 1975 first-grade data hold for later years and other grades. This brief note makes no attempt, however, to examine the entire range of factors influencing student performance, failure, attendance rates, and the like; rather, I focus on the specific question of how exposure to radio affects propensity for failure.

Other chapters in this volume report comprehensively on the effect of the radio mathematics lessons on student learning (Searle & Galda, 1980) and on other variables, including failure propensity (George, 1980). The analysis presented here differs from that of George in that it decomposes the effect of the radio lessons on failure propensity into, first, an indirect effect through its influence on achievement and, second, a direct effect. This decomposition is essential, as we shall see, to an understanding of the mechanisms of the influence of the radio lessons on failure.

1. THE DATA AND THE PROBLEM

The data we use are from the summative evaluation of the Radio Mathematics Project that was undertaken by Stanford University's Institute for Mathematical Studies in the Social Sciences (IMSSS). The chapters in this volume by Searle and Galda (1980) and George (1980) describe the procedures for treatment assignment and data collection in detail. To highlight the main point of this note, we deal only with the variables central to understanding the radio mathematics lessons' impact on failure propensity; Table 1 lists and defines these variables and gives their means and standard deviations. Data are available for Grades 1 and 2 for the 1976 school year and for Grade 3 for the 1977 school year. For evaluation, schools were randomly assigned to receive radio lessons or not for the first- and third-grade studies, but not for the second grade.[3] At each grade level, the students following the

---

[2] Searle, Sheehan, González, and George (1978) provide a more detailed description of the patterns of student failure and repetition in Nicaraguan schools and of some of the factors influencing those patterns. Galda and González (1980), in a chapter in this volume, provide more descriptive information on the factors influencing teachers' decisions concerning student promotion. Haddad (1979) reviews the literature on the consequences of different promotion practices, and UNESCO (1980) provides an up-to-date account of the extent of student failures (and dropouts) in 40 countries of Africa, 24 countries of Latin America, and 33 countries of Asia and Oceania.

[3] The sequence for production and evaluation of the radio mathematics materials at the first-grade level was that the curriculum was developed and pretested in 1975 in a

TABLE 1

Overall Sample Statistics of **POST**, **PRE**, and **RADIO**

Variable	Definition	Grade	N	Mean	SD
PRE	Mathematics pretest	1	954	20.96	4.61
	score	2	776	54.61	9.18
		3	536	77.36	10.26
RADIO	1 if student is	1	2,021	.624	.484
	in radio class,	2	1,296	.462	.499
	0 otherwise	3	965	.599	.491
POST	Mathematics posttest	1	882	46.67	14.97
	score	2	712	79.69	11.16
		3	558	63.24	10.66
FAIL	1 if student fails,	1	1,956	.372	.484
	0 otherwise	2	1,257	.173	.378
		3	876	.177	.382

radio lessons were receiving the broadcasts for the first time in the year of the study.

Table 2 compares the mean values of the variables **PRE, POST,** and **FAIL** for the radio and control groups.[4] The highly significant difference between pretest scores for the radio and control groups in the second grade underscores the nonrandom nature of the treatment assignment at that grade level; the near equality of pretest scores for Grades 1 and 3 suggests that the randomization was fairly good at those grade levels. Two other points emerge clearly from Table 2. The first is that radio students perform much better on the posttest, as has consistently been found in project evaluations. The second is that the failure rates are virtually identical for the two groups. Since there was random assignment of schools to the radio treatment at the first- and third-grade levels, it seems reasonable to

---

group of schools to which there was (nonrandomly) assigned a comparison group of schools; in 1976 the revised curriculum materials were evaluated with a random assignment of schools to the radio condition. Thus, the 1975 first-grade study of failure reported in Jamison (1978) was based on a nonrandom comparison in the curriculum development year; the 1976 first-grade study, reported here, is based on random assignment and the revised curriculum. Curriculums at the second- and third-grade levels were not revised, but by 1977, when the third-grade curriculum was being developed, there was random assignment of schools to the radio condition even in the development year.

[4] This analysis is based on the subsample of the data, described in Table 2, for which there were no missing values for **PRE, POST, FAIL,** and **RADIO.**

TABLE 2

Mean Values of **POST, FAIL,** and **PRE**
in Radio and Control Groups

Variable	Grade	N	Control	Radio	t^a
PRE	1	615	20.76	21.26	−1.42
	2	606	52.15	57.80	−7.97
	3	400	77.86	77.23	.61
POST	1	615	39.44	53.38	−13.28
	2	606	76.70	83.91	−8.48
	3	400	61.28	68.15	−6.64
FAIL	1	615	.232	.224	.23
	2	606	.136	.131	.18
	3	400	.106	.079	.91

[a] This is the t statistic for testing the significance of the difference in means between the control and radio groups.

conclude that radio has no net influence on failure rates. This contradicts my findings from the 1975 first-grade data.[5] It also poses the problem of *why,* when radio is having the strong effect that it does on achievement, radio has no apparent effect on failure rates.

There are at least three plausible explanations for why radio improves the posttest score without reducing failure rates:

1. The performance of students in mathematics, as measured by the evaluation posttest (the results of which the teachers did *not* know), is unimportant in influencing the teachers' decisions to fail a child or not.

2. Exposure to the radio mathematics lessons has the effect of improving student performance in mathematics only at the cost of hurting it in other subjects (e.g., by reducing the time or attention paid the other subjects). In this line of thinking, increases in failure rate from reduced performance in other subjects would offset reductions from improved performance in mathematics.

3. Either explicitly or implicitly, teachers have in mind an "appropriate" failure rate for any given grade level. If the performance of all students goes up, teachers simply raise their cutoff point for failure to maintain approximately the same failure percentage.

---

[5] Even with the 1975 first-grade data, the failure rate for the radio students (46%) was higher than for the controls (44%). The multivariate analysis of failure determinants corrected for the fact that in the 1975 nonrandomized study the radio group had systematically more of the various characteristics increasing failure probability; after correction, it was found that radio had a net negative effect on failure propensity.

Unfortunately, the project lacked resources to gather data on student performance in subjects other than mathematics, so assessing the second hypothesis is difficult. However, the first-grade failure rates reported in Table 2 had become available by late 1977 and suggested the importance of testing for adverse effects of radio mathematics lessons on other subjects; and in 1978 a limited effort was made to address this issue. The project lessons were being evaluated at four grade levels in that year, and for second graders the evaluation included administration of a Spanish test. Searle and Galda (1980, Table 17) report the results of this test and conclude that there was no difference between the performance of the radio and that of the control groups. Though this limited testing is scarcely definitive, it does suggest that the second hypothesis is an inadequate explanation of why radio does not reduce failure rates. The next section looks further at the determinants of failure to assist in judging between the first and third hypotheses.

2. DETERMINANTS OF FAILURE

If radio does not reduce failure rates because the performance of students on the mathematics posttest measures nothing relevant to the teachers' failure decisions (the first hypothesis), then the regressions predicting failure propensity should show no significant effect of either radio or the posttest score. If, on the other hand, higher posttest scores result in lower failure probabilities, then the effect of radio in the failure regression must be to *increase* failure probability in order for the net effect of radio to be near zero after allowing for its failure-reducing effect (through the posttest score). This would be consistent with either the second or the third hypothesis. It is for this reason that it is important to decompose the effect of radio into its indirect effect through posttest score and its direct (or other) effects; Figure 1 illustrates the highly simplified model that we use to do this. The experimental (i.e., random treatment assignment) nature of the data for Grades 1 and 3 legitimates this simplification. So, too, does the fact that George's (1980) analysis using a broad range of covariates yields results close to these where specifications overlap.

Tables 3 and 4 present the main empirical findings; Table 3 shows the determinants of posttest score, and Table 4 shows the logit analysis of the determinants of failure propensity. In order to facilitate comparisons across grade levels, the pre- and posttest scores have been standardized to have a mean of zero and a standard deviation of one at each grade level; these standardized variables are labeled **SPRE** and **SPOST**.

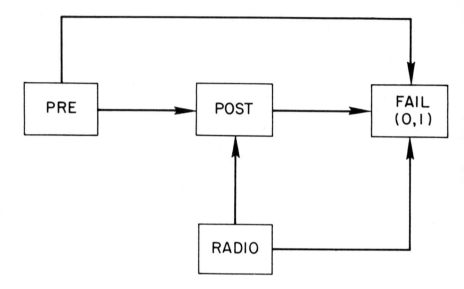

FIGURE 1. Simplified model of the determinants of student failure.

TABLE 3

Regression Determinants
of Posttest Scores

Independent variables	Grade		
	1	2	3
RADIO	.88	.24	.68
	(14.9)	(4.0)	(8.9)
SPRE	.50	.66	.60
	(16.0)	(22.5)	(15.7)
Constant	−.46	‚08	−.21
R^2	.45	.51	.44
N	615	606	400

Note. The regressions reported are ordinary least squares estimates of linear specifications in which the dependent variable, **SPOST,** is the standardized posttest score. The *t* statistic for each regression coefficient is reported in parentheses beneath it.

TABLE 4

Regression Determinants of End-of-year Failure

Independent variables	Grade					
	1		2		3	
	A	B	A	B	A	B
RADIO	−.044 (−.226)	1.46 (5.19)	−.036 (−.15)	.609 (2.22)	−.319 (−.892)	−.07 (−.179)
SPRE		−.281 (−2.19)		−.088 (−.492)		−.317 (−1.44)
SPOST		−1.54 (−9.05)		−.818 (−4.48)		−.449 (−1.96)
Constant	−1.20	−2.47	−1.85	−2.36	−2.13	−2.37
χ^2 of estimate	.05	173.7	.02	47.97	.82	16.65
N	615	615	606	606	400	400

Note. The regressions reported are maximum likelihood estimates of a logit specification in which the dependent variable, FAIL, takes the value 1 if the student fails at year-end and the value 0 if he or she passes. The asymptotic t value for each regression coefficient, a measure of its statistical significance, is reported in parentheses beneath the coefficient.

Table 3 shows more clearly than does Table 2 the strong impact of the radio mathematics lessons on student achievement. The effect is weakest at Grade 2, but radio students still do almost a quarter of a standard deviation better; in Grades 1 and 3, the improvements are .88 and .68 standard deviations, respectively. Searle and Galda (1980) and George (1980) treat these matters in far more detail.

Table 4 reports the determinants of end-of-year failure. For each grade level it shows (in the columns labeled 'A') the effect of radio alone on failure propensity; in the 'B' columns it shows the effect of radio and posttest, controlling for pretest. The radio coefficients in the 'A' columns show that the failure rates are about the same in both radio and control schools; in the 'B' columns, the radio coefficients are larger than in the 'A' columns, and, for Grades 1 and 2, they are positive and statistically significant. For all three grades the coefficient on SPOST is negative and statistically significant, though the effect is substantially larger for Grades 1 and 2; thus, higher levels of mathematics performance, as measured by the posttest, do reduce (and rather strongly) the likelihood that the student will be failed. These coefficients provide firm evidence against our first hypothesis as an explanation for the small net effect of radio on student failure, and, since radio students did as well on the second-grade Spanish test as did controls, it seems improbable that the second hypothesis is correct. The third hypothesis, however, is plausible: When students' mathematics performance improved from exposure to radio, their teachers set higher standards, and this resulted in little net change in the failure rate.

Table 5 shows results of calculations of the total (direct and indirect) effect of radio on failure probability using the estimated equations reported in the 'B' columns of Tables 3 and 4. These estimated failure rates control for possible preexisting differences between radio and control groups and thus provide a superior estimate of the true effect. While at each grade level the failure rates reported in Table 2 favor the radio groups (though by only a small and statistically insignificant amount), the estimated failure rates in Table 5 all favor the control groups. Again, however, the differences are very small—leading consistently to the conclusion that radio affects failure rates only negligibly. My earlier findings—that the radio mathematics lessons reduced failure rates at the first-grade level in the first year of the project—thus fails to conform to the pattern of results reported here. Possibly the teachers of the first-grade radio students in 1975 were atypical in being less inclined than the average to maintain a constant failure rate when mathematics performance of their students was improving.

TABLE 5

Effects of Radio
on Failure Propensity

Grade	Failure probability	
	Without radio	With radio
1	.186	.199
2	.094	.134
3	.078	.097

Note. This table shows the estimated expected value of the failure probability under the assumption that pretest scores are distributed in the population as a whole in the same way as they are in this sample.

3. CONCLUSIONS

This note has addressed the question of why the Radio Mathematics Project, despite its strongly favorable effect on student learning, has no apparent effect on the high failure rates in Nicaraguan elementary schools. The note examined three possible explanations for this phenomenon:

1. The mathematics performance of individual students has little influence on teachers' decisions concerning whether the students are promoted.

2. Exposure to radio mathematics lessons has the effect of improving the mathematics performance of students only at the cost of reducing their performance in other subjects.

3. Teachers have in mind an "appropriate" failure rate, for each class as a whole, that is relatively uninfluenced by the average performance of the class.

The evidence reported here strongly repudiates the first explanation; and evidence reported elsewhere in this volume goes against the second explanation, which was in any case implausible. We can conclude, therefore, that when students' mathematics performance improved from exposure to Radio Mathematics Project lessons, their teachers set higher standards and this resulted in little net change in the failure rate.

REFERENCES

Galda, K., & González, J. Teachers' promotion decisions in Nicaraguan first through fourth grades. In J. Friend, B. Searle, & P. Suppes (Eds.), *Radio Mathematics in Nicaragua*. Stanford, Calif.: Stanford University, Institute for Mathematical Studies in the Social Sciences, 1980.

George, E. I. Exploring the effects of the Radio Mathematics Project on school-related variables. In J. Friend, B. Searle, & P. Suppes (Eds.), *Radio Mathematics in Nicaragua*. Stanford, Calif.: Stanford University, Institute for Mathematical Studies in the Social Sciences, 1980.

Haddad, W. D. *Educational and economic effects of promotion and repetition practices* (World Bank Staff Working Paper No. 319). Washington, D.C.: The World Bank, 1979.

Jamison, D. T. Radio education and student repetition in Nicaragua. In P. Suppes, B. Searle, & J. Friend (Eds.), *The Radio Mathematics Project: Nicaragua, 1976–1977*. Stanford, Calif.: Stanford University, Institute for Mathematical Studies in the Social Sciences, 1978.

Searle, B., & Galda, K. Measurement of the effect of radio mathematics lessons on student achievement. In J. Friend, B. Searle, & P. Suppes (Eds.), *Radio Mathematics in Nicaragua*. Stanford, Calif.: Stanford University, Institute for Mathematical Studies in the Social Sciences, 1980.

Searle, B., Sheehan, J., González, J., & George, E. Patterns of promotion and wastage for Nicaraguan first-grade students. In P. Suppes, B. Searle, & J. Friend (Eds.), *The Radio Mathematics Project: Nicaragua, 1976–1977.* Stanford, Calif.: Stanford University, Institute for Mathematical Studies in the Social Sciences, 1978.

Searle, B., Friend, J., & Suppes, P. *The Radio Mathematics Project: Nicaragua, 1974–1975.* Stanford, Calif.: Stanford University, Institute for Mathematical Studies in the Social Sciences, 1976.

UNESCO. *Wastage in primary and general secondary education: A statistical study of trends and patterns in repetition and dropout.* Paris: UNESCO, Office of Statistics, 1980. (Forthcoming)

From the beginning of the project, the radio mathematics lessons were seen as a vehicle for reaching the students in their schools, not in their homes. The lessons were intended to be taken sequentially, under the supervision of a classroom teacher who could work with the radio teacher to present a complete, well-rounded program of mathematics instruction within a formal school setting. The needs of a casual listening audience outside the schools, with diverse backgrounds and fewer incentives to follow the complete course of instruction, were initially not addressed.

As time went on, however, we became increasingly aware that the lessons were attracting an out-of-school audience. We received several letters from housewives who enclosed workpapers they had completed during the radio broadcasts. We heard rumors of a local vendor who daily gathered together all children in his neighborhood who were not in school to listen to the mathematics programs on his small radio receiver. One teacher told us that all of her students' parents listened to the radio programs at home.

This kind of evidence prompted us to make some alterations in our lesson format in Grades 3 and 4 (see chap. 2) to accommodate the out-of-school audience, even though we still had no good idea of the extent of that audience or whether they were regular or casual listeners.

This chapter reports the results of a small survey of that unanticipated but welcome home audience.

Chapter 8

SURVEY OF THE HOME LISTENING AUDIENCE
OF THE RADIO MATHEMATICS PROJECT

Marvin Saballos, Klaus Galda,
and José González

THIS CHAPTER presents the results of an informal investigation into the size and other characteristics of the home listening audience of the Nicaragua Radio Mathematics Project. The study was prompted, first, by the many letters received from students in nonparticipating schools and from individuals who, on their own initiative, follow the lessons and, second, by the results of a listener survey that showed Radiodifusora Nacional among the top 10 radio stations for three programs: a folk music program, a question and answer show, and the Radio Mathematics Project lessons. The survey, conducted by a private consulting firm, KONSULTEC, between February 20 and March 12, 1978, was one in a series that provides regular information to radio stations about their audiences in the capital city of Managua.

These two kinds of evidence about informal listening motivated the administrators of the project to investigate the size of the home listening audience and to compare the numbers of listeners in rural and urban communities, in lower and middle class areas, and in communities in which experimental schools were and were not located. The study did not use rigorous survey methods and should be interpreted in the light of the following design limitations:

1. The geographical areas sampled were not randomly chosen;
2. The homes within each neighborhood were not randomly sampled;
3. The interviewers were not trained in interviewing techniques.

In the following sections we discuss some special characteristics of the radio lessons that might affect home listening and then we turn to a description of the survey and the results.

1. THE RADIO MATHEMATICS LESSONS

The radio mathematics lessons for first and second grades were designed solely for formal, in-school use. Consequently, these lessons are not entirely appropriate for informal use by a home listening audience. For example, first-grade radio lessons require students to use worksheets; the parts of the lesson that refer to exercises or pictures printed on the worksheet would be of little use to the listener who does not have a worksheet in hand.[1] Although they do not require worksheets, second-grade lessons frequently refer to exercises and drawings put on the chalkboard by the teacher prior to the radio broadcast; these exercises and drawings are copied from a teacher's guide that the project supplies only to experimental schools, so here again, a home listening audience would have difficulty following parts of the lessons. During the course of its work the project strategy about lesson use shifted. Thus, while school children remain the major target audience for the program, the radio lessons for third grade and fourth grade were designed to be self-contained, so that both classroom students and other listeners could use the lessons without supporting materials.

During the period of the survey, August 1978, lessons for all four grades were broadcast every weekday morning according to the following schedule: Grade 1 at 9:00, Grade 2 at 8:30, Grade 3 at 10:30, and Grade 4 at 11:00.

2. SAMPLING PROCEDURES

The survey was conducted in communities in three departments (provinces) of Nicaragua—Masaya, Granada, and Managua—that were chosen because of their accessibility and the project staff's familiarity with them. A different type of comparison was made in each department. In Masaya a comparison was made of communities in which there is an experimental school and those in which the school did not use radio lessons; all of these communities are rural and lower class. Also in Granada communities with and without experimental schools were compared, but these communities were all urban and mixed middle and lower class. In Managua, where there are no communities with experimental schools, the comparison was between middle class and lower class neighborhoods.

---

[1] Worksheets will be used less frequently in future first-grade radio lessons; see Suppes, Searle, and Friend, 1978, p. 32.

For the study, a community (or neighborhood) was defined as the group of homes around a school. The communities were chosen in a two-step process. First, a nonexhaustive list of eligible communities was made, using school names to identify the communities. For example, the Masaya list consisted of rural schools in lower class areas of Masaya including both those that did and those that did not use radio lessons. Then, two or three communities were taken at random from each list to form the appropriate subsample.

Table 1 summarizes the characteristics of the six subsamples and shows the number of homes surveyed. The table introduces a mnemonic device for identifying subsamples that will be used in presenting results. For example, the first subsample, labeled R-L-R, is rural (R), lower class (L), and around a school that uses radio lessons (R). In the remaining labels, U stands for urban, X for mixed middle and lower class, M for middle class, and N for communities with schools that do not use radio.

Because Managua was not part of the project experimental area, its communities are identified as nonradio; however, the survey showed that some Managua schools do in fact use the radio mathematics lessons.

The number of homes surveyed in each community depended primarily on practical considerations. Since a fixed period of time was allotted for visiting each community, more homes were sampled in

TABLE 1

Number and Characteristics of Households Surveyed

Subsample	Characteristics				Number (%) of households
	Department	Location	SES	Radio/ nonradio	
R-L-R	Masaya	Rural	Low	Radio	71 (14.9)
R-L-N	Masaya	Rural	Low	Nonradio	32 (6.7)
U-X-R	Granada	Urban	Middle/low	Radio	62 (13.0)
U-X-N	Granada	Urban	Middle/low	Nonradio	48 (10.1)
U-M-N	Managua	Urban	Middle	Nonradio	77 (16.2)
U-L-N	Managua	Urban	Low	Nonradio	186 (39.1)
TOTAL					476 (100.0)

densely populated areas than elsewhere. Two interviewers were assigned to each community. They started their sampling with homes near the local school. A home was sampled if, in the opinion of the interviewer, there was at least one resident at home capable of responding to the questions on the survey instrument.

3. THE SURVEY INSTRUMENT

The survey instrument was an open-ended questionnaire with 13 items (see Appendix A), designed to do the following.

1. Determine whether any residents listened to radio lessons at home or at school. (Questions 1, 2, 3, and 10)

2. Determine how many individuals, and of what age and sex, listened to radio lessons. (Questions 1, 2, 3, and 11)

3. Check the reliability of the responses by asking for details about lesson presentation, grade of the lesson, and time and day of the transmission. This also served to differentiate between the project's lessons and those of another radio program. (Questions 4, 5, 6, and 7)

4. Verify by means of the grade and name of the school which schools were actually listening to the project's radio lessons. (Questions 12 and 13)

5. Determine the socioeconomic status of the home sampled. (Observation)

4. RESULTS

Responses to questionnaire items allowed classification of households into six categories, five of which indicate some degree of listening to mathematics programs. (Mathematics lessons are also broadcast as part of an adult education program sponsored by the Catholic Church.) The categories are defined as follows.

Category	Definition
Yes, frequently.	Households in which individuals listen to radio lessons every weekday or several days of the week.
Yes, sometimes.	Households in which individuals listen to radio lessons in a fortuitous or haphazard fashion.
Yes, in the past.	Households in which individuals have listened to radio lessons in the past, but no longer do so.

Yes, only in school.   Households with children who listen to radio lessons at school, but not at home.

Yes, another program.   Households in which individuals listen to a different radio mathematics program.

No, we do not listen.   Households in which no one listens either to the Radio Mathematics Project or to any other instructional radio program with mathematics lessons.

Table 2 indicates that of the 476 households sampled, 42% have occupants who listen or have listened in the past to radio lessons from one source or another. Close to half of these households (20% of the total sample) listen frequently to the Radio Mathematics Project lessons. Note that of the total sample, 35% listen frequently or sometimes and of those falling in one of the five "Yes" categories, 82% listen frequently or sometimes. A breakdown of the "frequent" listeners indicates that 54 of the 93 households (58%) listen to radio mathematics lessons five days a week. The remaining 39 households listen regularly but not every day.

TABLE 2

Listening Categories by Subsample

Subsample	Number (%) of households						
	Category						Total
	Fre-quently	Some-times	In the past	Only in school	Another program	Do not listen	
R-L-R	27 (38)	7 (10)	3 (4)	2 (3)	0 (0)	32 (45)	71
R-L-N	9 (28)	1 (3)	0 (0)	0 (0)	1 (3)	21 (66)	32
U-X-R	11 (18)	17 (27)	0 (0)	0 (0)	1 (2)	33 (53)	62
U-X-N	8 (17)	7 (15)	0 (0)	0 (0)	1 (2)	32 (66)	48
U-M-N	3 (4)	4 (5)	0 (0)	0 (0)	2 (3)	68 (88)	77
U-L-N	35 (19)	35 (19)	2 (1)	5 (3)	18 (10)	91 (48)	186
TOTAL	93 (20)	71 (15)	5 (1)	7 (1)	23 (5)	277 (58)	476

In Table 3 (and subsequently) the data are collapsed into three categories. Households that responded "Yes, frequently" are called the regular audience. Households that have at one time or another listened to instructional radio (all other "Yes" responses) are called the casual audience. The remaining households are called nonlisteners.

The results presented in Table 3 allow the pairwise comparisons implicit in the initial design. In rural, lower class communities, the total listening population is 20% greater in communities in which there are experimental schools; this difference is evenly divided between the regular and the casual audience. In the urban, mixed middle and lower class communities, the presence of an experimental school appears to have increased only the casual audience. In the urban, nonradio neighborhoods of Managua, listening is about four times as likely in lower class households as in middle class households.

The largest regular audience (38%) is found in rural, lower class communities surrounding experimental schools. This group contains the community of Los Pocitos, whose primary school has worked with the project for four years and whose teacher is an enthusiastic supporter of project lessons. Fifteen of the 20 homes surveyed in Los Pocitos listen to radio mathematics lessons frequently.

The lowest percentage of regular listeners was found in the middle class, urban neighborhoods of Managua, while lower class Managua neighborhoods showed the highest percentage of casual listeners.

TABLE 3

Listening Patterns in Community Subsamples

Subsample	Percentage of households		
	Regular audience	Casual audience	Non-listeners
R-L-R	38.0	16.9	45.1
R-L-N	28.1	6.3	65.6
U-X-R	17.7	29.0	53.2
U-X-N	16.7	16.7	66.7
U-M-N	3.9	7.8	88.3
U-L-N	18.8	32.2	48.9
TOTAL	19.5	22.3	58.2

In Table 4, comparisons for the dimensions of interest are presented for pooled data. The results suggest that regular listeners are more likely to be found in rural rather than urban communities, in lower class rather than middle class communities, and in communities in which there is a school that uses the radio programs for instruction. The results also suggest that when rural people listen they are more likely to listen regularly, but when urban people listen they are more likely to listen irregularly.

Respondents were asked what the grade level was of the lessons they listened to. This information was of interest because of the difficulty of completely understanding first- and second-grade lessons without having worksheets or teacher's guides. Of the 93 households that listened regularly, 29% listened to first-grade lessons, 26% to second grade, 39% to third grade, 29% to fourth grade, and 6% could not identify the grade level. (The percentages sum to more than 100 because some households listened to more than one grade.) Thus, a surprisingly large number of households listened to lessons that had not been written with a home audience in mind.

The questionnaire item about the presence of children in the household who listened to radio lessons in school uncovered the fact that one school in Granada designated by the project as a control school was using radio lessons and that approximately 3% of the 186 households surveyed in the middle class, urban neighborhoods of

TABLE 4

Variation in Listening Patterns
by Community Characteristic

Characteristic	Percentage of households		
	Regular audience	Casual audience	Non-listeners
Location			
Rural	35.0	13.6	51.5
Urban	15.3	24.7	60.0
SES			
Low	24.6	25.6	49.8
Mid/low	17.3	23.6	59.1
Mid	3.9	7.8	88.3
Radio/nonradio			
Radio	28.6	22.5	48.9
Nonradio	16.0	22.2	61.8

Managua had children who listened to lessons at school. On further inquiry it was found that these children attend two private schools and two public schools.

5. CONCLUSIONS

This informal investigation of home listening provides support for the great educational potential of radio in Nicaragua. In summary, 37% of the households surveyed reported listening (at some time) to the Radio Mathematics Project lessons. This is a sizable audience for an educational radio program, and its size is particularly surprising in view of the fact that the project does not advertise its lessons and uses a station with a generally small listening audience.

Almost half the households listening to radio lessons do so regularly, with the majority of these households listening every day of the week. Although the remaining households do not listen regularly, almost all are familiar enough with the program to be able to identify the grade levels of the lessons they listen to.

The study found that rural and lower class households are more likely to listen regularly than urban and middle class households and that, at least in rural areas, the presence of a school using the radio lessons stimulates listening. The experience in Los Pocitos suggests that a local teacher can have a significant influence on the listening pattern in the community the school serves.

Evaluation studies (Searle, Matthews, Suppes, & Friend, 1978) have shown that the Radio Mathematics Project lessons significantly raise the achievement levels of the school children using the program. The effectiveness of the lessons for the home audience has not yet been demonstrated, but the popularity of the program suggests that the lessons could serve to reach the large rural, lower class adult population that has not in the past received an adequate primary education.

REFERENCES

Searle, B., Matthews, P., Suppes, P., & Friend, J.   Formal evaluation of the radio mathematics instructional program. In T. Cook (Ed.), *Evaluation studies review annual* (Vol. 3). Beverly Hills, Calif.: Sage, 1978.
Suppes, P., Searle, B., & Friend, J. (Eds.), *The Radio Mathematics Project: Nicaragua, 1976–1977.* Stanford, Calif.: Stanford University, Institute for Mathematical Studies in the Social Sciences, 1978.

APPENDIX A

Home Listening Audience Survey

Community: _____

City: _____

Location: _____

1. Have you heard the mathematics classes that are broadcast over the radio? (If yes, go to question 2; if no, go to question 3.)
   _____
   _____

2. What other persons in the home listen to the Radio Mathematics Project? (Continue with question 4.)
   _____
   _____

Children	Men	Women
(0–15 years old)	(older than 15)	(older than 15)
_____	_____	_____

3. Is there any person in the home who listens to the Radio Mathematics Project lessons? (If no, go to question 10; if yes, continue with question 4.)
   _____
   _____

Children	Men	Women
(0–15 years old)	(older than 15)	(older than 15)
_____	_____	_____

245

4. On what station?

_____

_____

5. At what time do you listen?

_____

_____

6. To what grades do you listen?

_____

_____

7. On what days do you listen?

_____

_____

8. What problems have you had with the lessons of the Radio Mathematics Project?

_____

_____

_____

_____

9. What do you like about the lessons of the Radio Mathematics Project?

_____

_____

_____

_____

10. In school, do some of the children in your home listen to the lessons of the Radio Mathematics Project? (If no, finish the interview; if yes, continue with question 11.)

_____

_____

11. How many of the children?

12. In what grade(s)?

13. What is the name of the school?

Observations:

INDEX

Page numbers in italics refer to the reference lists at the ends of the chapters.